Methods of Presenting Fieldwork Data

18

Methods of Presenting Fieldwork Data

**Peter St John
and Dave Richardson**

THE GEOGRAPHICAL ASSOCIATION

ISBN 1 899085 49 1

First published 1989
Reprinted 1995, 1996
First revised edition 1997
Impression number 10 9 8 7 6 5 4 3 2 1
Year 2000 1999 1998 1997

Published by the Geographical Association, 160 Solly Street, Sheffield S1 4BF. The GA is a registered charity: no 313129

The Publications Officer of the GA would be happy to hear from other potential authors who have ideas for geography books. You may contact the Publications Officer via the Geographical Association at the address above. The views expressed in this publication are those of the authors and do not necessarily represent those of the Geographical Association.

Acknowledgements

The authors would like to thank the following people for their help with this book:

Mr E.E. Jones, the previous Warden of Lancashire's Field Study Centre, Hothersall Lodge, for his continual support and for supplying the photographs;

Mrs E Kenny, for typing and retyping the original drafts, always with a smile;

J M Fallas for the cartoons;

the staff and students of many Lancashire schools and colleges who indicated the need for just such a manual, and who fully field-tested the contents over a number of years.

Cover photograph: A-level students carrying out a river study on Langden Beck, Forest of Bowland Photo: Dave Richardson
Frontispiece: Students field sketching. Photo: Patrick Bailey.

Diagrams: Paul Coles
Design: White Line Publishing Services
Typesetting: Ledgard Jepson
Cover design: Chris Hand
Printed and bound in England by The Thanet Press

CONTENTS

INTRODUCTION

Fieldwork plays an important part in any geography, biology or environmental studies course and, therefore, selecting the most appropriate method of presenting the field data is as important as collecting the data itself. Many existing texts aid students in setting up their fieldwork investigations and guide them through the various techniques of data collection. This book is designed to complement those publications by:

- enabling fieldworkers to use their imagination in selecting the most appropriate techniques for the type of data collected;
- illustrating the wide range of graphical and cartographical techniques available; and
- making students confident in the use of different, and often more sophisticated, techniques (many of which appear as data response questions in their final examinations).

Table 1 illustrates the variety of techniques described in the sections of this book and indicates when each technique should be used. Students should 'dip' into this manual for inspiration rather than use it as the definitive document on the subject.

The exact use of each technique depends on the precise nature of the data. Each technique appears whenever possible under the standard headings of 'When to use', 'Examples', 'Method of construction' and 'Worked examples'. In some cases an additional section on drawbacks/criticisms is included. A 'Glossary of terms' explains the meaning of emboldened terms which appear throughout the manual.

Students wishing to further their fieldwork analysis by the use of simple statistical techniques should consult the companion volume *Statistical Methods of Analysing Fieldwork Data*, also published by the GA.

Table 1: Type of information

Type of information	Technique	Page(s)
1 Introducing the student to the subject matter or area	Field sketches Tabulation Base maps Flow diagrams	8 10 55 12
2 The organisation of raw data into a manageable form	Tabulation Ways of classifying data Use of logarithms	10 14 41
3 Representation of sequential data that changes over time	Line graphs Circular graphs Pictograms	16 38 18
4 Observed data at specific sites or locations that have definite component categories	Barcharts and histograms Pyramid graphs Multiple and composite graphs Mirror graphs Reverse bars Pie graphs	20-25 22 24 + 25 23 40 26-28
5 Representing connections between two sets of data	Scattergraphs/correlation graphs Mirror graphs	29 23
6 Representing data that shows a definite orientation	Rose diagrams Polar co-ordinates	34-36 39-40
7 Data that is composed of a number of elements that total 100%	Triangular graphs (three elements) Composite bargraphs Block graphs	37 25 51-52
8 Where measurements of side views have been taken	Profiles Cross sections	44-45 45-48
9 Where data has been collected either continuously or at intervals along a sample line (a transect)	Scattergraphs Profiles and cross sections Mapping and divided bars Kite diagrams Block graphs	29 44-48 50-52 52-53 53-54

10 Data has been collected to show spatial variation	Base maps which then use the following:
	  Dot maps
	  Symbols and proportional symbols
	  Choropleths and isopleths
	  Location quotient
		
		55-56
		57-60
		62-66
		67-68

11 Where data has been collected to show spatial variation of movements and flows	Composite bars Flow lines Desire lines	69 70-71 72

1: FIELD SKETCHES

These are exactly what the title suggests: sketches made in the field showing a landform or feature of interest. A good photograph of the same feature may be useful but it can never be a real substitute for a well-drawn and clearly-labelled field sketch. Drawing a field sketch serves a number of purposes. It will:

1   Compel the observer to look more closely at the feature and to carefully record their observations at that particular time and place.

2   Allow the observer to select, emphasise and even omit whichever details they wish. A photograph may show too much detail but a good field sketch should omit the irrelevant and emphasise the relevant.

3   Indicate to your students that it is easier to use a field sketch than a photograph as a base for recording data in the field. By labelling their field sketch students should intend to convey information such as location or explanation of features. No other method of presenting fieldwork data, graph, map or transect, is able to communicate this type of information.

4   Create a summary of the student's observations made at that time in a dramatic and vivid way. They can add a visual impact to any fieldwork project.

Field sketches must look like the feature depicted. This is no easy matter as very few landscapes are simple and not all people are natural artists. With the help of the following tips and plenty of practice, either in the field or from pictures/slides in the classroom, most students can reach an acceptable standard of sketching.

Tips

1   The most common error in sketching is to over-exaggerate the vertical (e.g. hills are commonly drawn too high). To overcome this divide the page into three equal parts by drawing two lines across it. These can then act as guidelines. Alternatively, squares or hand-drawn grids may be used.

2   Decide on the boundaries of what you want to draw. A natural feature such as a row of trees, a spur of land, etc., may often be used in this context. Alternatively, a cardboard frame held vertically can be used to define the area and give an idea of scale. If a transparent sheet is inserted into this frame the major features may be 'traced' using a felt tip pen. This outline can then be transferred onto paper at a later date.

3   First sketch the horizon followed by the other major features. Hold the pencil at arms length to work out the rough **proportions** of the major features. If this part of the outline is done well the rest will follow more easily.

4   Fill in the required detail section by section and omit the irrelevant. If you choose to use a grid complete each square in turn until you have built up the whole picture.

Note: Not every minute detail is necessary, include just enough to illustrate the points you are trying to make.

5 Shading and lines can be used to show slope and angle to great effect. Symbols for features such as woodlands, fields, water, etc., can be devised (see Figure 1.1). If you choose to add symbols you may need to include a key.

6 Give your sketch a full and detailed title. This tells the reader the location and what you are trying to show. The title should include details such as:
   • where the sketch was drawn (grid references),
   • the direction the observer was facing, and
   • what you are trying to show (land use, physical features, settlement pattern, etc.).

7 All features must be labelled in full or, if appropriate, include a key. Where possible label each feature in a different colour or type of print. All these factors help to orientate the sketch for the reader.

It is possible to produce sketch maps of rivers, glacial features or beach deposit using the same principles as those outlined above.

Worked example

Figure 1.1: Langden Brook looking downstream

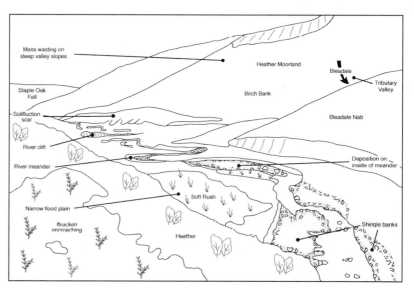

Figure 1.2: Field sketch of the main valley features from the same viewpoint

2: TABULATION

Because the nature of the data tends to dictate the nature of the table there are no set rules for constructing tables. However, it is important to make tables of data clear and concise. This applies to tables compiled in the field and those done as an integral part of the overall fieldwork project. Well structured tables show the reader where much of the information came from and how it was collected. Such tables can be a worthwhile method of representing data. The following suggestions will be helpful in the preparation and compilation of tables.

1   As with field sketches, tables must have a title and be fully labelled. It should be obvious to the reader what the table is trying to show and be unnecessary for them to search for further explanations in the text.

2   Wherever possible show the 'raw' data – the data collected in the field. This should appear as the first table in that particular section or inserted as an appendix and be referred to in the text. Values manipulated from this raw data (percentages, means, etc.) should then be put into a set of secondary tables.

3   One common fault is to try and put too much information onto one table. It is better to put summaries into separate tables.

4   Include totals for each row and column only if this detail is relevant. A grand total may be included in the bottom right hand corner (by addition of all the rows and columns) as a final check.

5   If the type of **totals** are different (**partial, accumulative, grand,** etc.) make sure they are clearly labelled, especially if they appear on the same table.

6   Where numbers have been converted in some way (e.g. into percentages or by formulae) show clearly what the conversions are and where the original data came from.

7   Units of measurement must be included at all times.

8   You may find it useful to leave space for later additions. It easier to extend the number of rows rather than the number of columns.

Tables 2.1 and 2.2 and Equation 2.1 illustrate some of the different types of tables and calculations that may be used for both the collection and the display of field data.

Worked examples

Table 2.1: Stream channel variables (normal flow) for Langden Beck, Lancashire

Channel variables	Site number									
	1	2	3	4	5	6	7	8	9	10
1 Distance downstream in winter in metres	200	1100	1900	2400	3100	3900	4200	5300	5900	6500
2 Long profile gradient in degrees	6.2	5.1	3.1	4.6	2.5	1.5	1.8	0.4	1.3	0.5
3 Mean velocity in metres per second	0.78	0.62	0.54	0.91	0.89	0.99	1.2	1.34	1.21	1.45
4 Cross section area – square metres	0.12	0.34	0.48	0.51	0.62	1.21	1.45	1.56	1.85	1.89
5 Discharge in Cumecs (3 x 4)	0.09	0.21	0.26	0.46	0.55	1.19	1.74	2.09	1.89	2.74
6 Wetted perimeter in metres	0.86	0.94	1.12	1.63	1.97	2.46	3.14	4.92	5.67	4.81
7 Hydraulic radius (4 ÷ 6)	0.14	0.36	0.43	0.31	0.31	0.49	0.46	0.32	0.33	0.39
8 Mean stone size (a axis) in millimetres	289	198	201	189	134	145	101	86	92	67
9 Sphericity index (after Krumbein)	0.36	0.32	0.56	0.65	0.54	0.64	0.72	0.53	0.78	0.75

Table 2.2: Spearman Rank Correlation Coefficient (distance downstream is correlated against long profile gradient using data from Table 2.1)

Variable A (distance downstream (m))	Rank	Variable B (long profile gradient(°))	Rank	Difference in ranks (d)	d^2
200	10	6.2	1	+9	81
1100	9	5.1	2	+7	49
1900	8	3.1	4	+4	16
2400	7	4.6	3	+4	16
3100	6	2.5	5	+1	1
3900	5	1.5	7	-2	4
4200	4	1.8	6	-2	4
5300	3	0.4	10	-7	49
5900	2	1.3	8	-6	36
6500	1	0.5	9	-8	64

Total (Σ) d^2 = 320

Equation 2.1

$$\text{Spearman rank (rho)} = 1 - \left(\frac{6.\Sigma d^2}{n^3 - n} \right)$$

where n = number of paired observations cubed.

therefore

$$\text{rho} = 1 - \left(\frac{6 \times 320}{1000 - 10} \right)$$

$$= 1 - \left(\frac{1920}{990} \right) \quad = -0.939$$

There are (n) degrees of freedom (10)

3: FLOW DIAGRAMS (SYSTEMS DIAGRAMS)

When to use

Many fieldwork projects are concerned with the investigation of a particular geographical or ecological process/system and it may be useful to show the system under investigation. This can be done either by means of an introduction to the work or, once the analysis has been completed, as a conclusion. One of the best ways of doing this graphically is by constructing a flow diagram (sometimes called a systems diagram). An example is shown in Figure 3.1.

Examples

Systems which can be shown in a diagrammatic form as flow charts include the following examples: slope, fluvial, marine and glacial processes, plant successions, woodland ecology, agricultural, industrial, settlement, and transport.

Method of construction

Most modern textbooks contain systems diagrams but it is far better for you as the fieldworker to construct your own because they relate to your own specific and unique study. Flow charts/systems diagrams should be constructed as follows:

1   Identify each of the stages in the system and write each one on a separate piece of paper. These are your stages or 'boxes'.

2   Identify where each stage (box) appears in the sequence and paste them onto another sheet of paper.

3   Draw in arrows to indicate where a relationship or flow exists between each of the stages (boxes).

With practice your students will be able to simply draw up their flow charts onto a single sheet of paper. However, the ordering of the stages is only achievable by careful forethought or even trial and error.

Note: These three stages give a simple diagram (see Figure 3.1 for an example) but it is possible to construct more complex diagrams called 'constellation diagrams'. As constellation diagrams are more complex and specific in nature a brief description and worked example are shown Appendix 2 (see page 74).

Worked example

Figure 3.1: Formation and development of a limestone pavement ecosystem

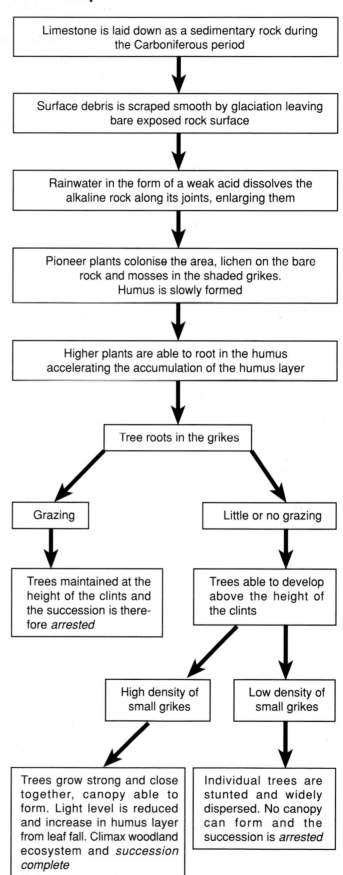

Limestone is laid down as a sedimentary rock during the Carboniferous period

↓

Surface debris is scraped smooth by glaciation leaving bare exposed rock surface

↓

Rainwater in the form of a weak acid dissolves the alkaline rock along its joints, enlarging them

↓

Pioneer plants colonise the area, lichen on the bare rock and mosses in the shaded grikes. Humus is slowly formed

↓

Higher plants are able to root in the humus accelerating the accumulation of the humus layer

↓

Tree roots in the grikes

Grazing | Little or no grazing

Trees maintained at the height of the clints and the succession is therefore *arrested* | Trees able to develop above the height of the clints

High density of small grikes | Low density of small grikes

Trees grow strong and close together, canopy able to form. Light level is reduced and increase in humus layer from leaf fall. Climax woodland ecosystem and *succession complete* | Individual trees are stunted and widely dispersed. No canopy can form and the succession is *arrested*

Data collected in the field (in preparation for analysis as part of a fieldwork investigation) often has to be processed before it can be used. For many of the techniques in this book the data must be classified before it can be graphed or mapped, e.g. choropleth mapping, flow lines. Several methods for putting 'raw' data into groups already exist.

The first step is to look at how the individual observations are spread across the range. This is best achieved by constructing a *dispersal diagram* as shown in Figure 4.1.

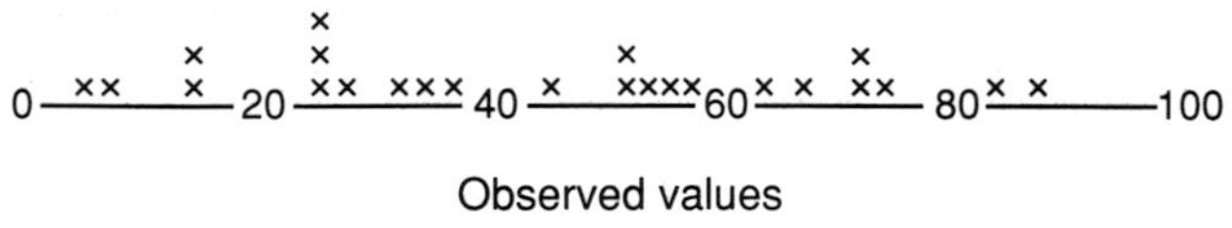

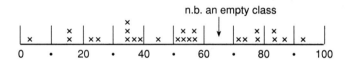

Observed values

Figure 4.1: Dispersal diagram

Fixed intervals
The data range is divided into regular size classes (0-9.9, 10-19.9, etc.). The frequency of occurrences in each of the classes is then noted (see Figure 4.2).

Figure 4.2: Divisions into regular size classes

This is the most common method used, however, if the points are unevenly distributed it can lead to some misleading representations (this is especially true of choropleth mapping - see Section 19, pages 62-63).

Percentile groupings
Groups are defined so that each contains an equal number of points. For example, if there are 25 observations and five categories then the first five points are placed in class 1, the second in class 2 and so on (see Figure 4.3).

Figure 4.3: Percentile groupings

This offers an improvement on the fixed intervals method because it overcomes the problems of the data being unevenly distributed. However, it can give a misleading impression by artificially dividing up clearly related clusters of points, for example, as at point A on Figure 4.3.

Arbitrary method (Figure 4.4)
Sometimes called the natural groupings method. Divisions are drawn in by eye according to natural clusters of points.

This method is useful for choropleth mapping as the final map gives a clear indication of reality. However, it is unsuitable for other techniques because the classes may be of uneven sizes and contain unequal numbers of data points (e.g. Figure 4.4).

Figure 4.4: Arbitrary groupings

Standard deviation classes

Descriptive statistics can be used to define the classes. A data set may be divided on the basis of its mean and standard deviation classes (e.g. Figure 4.5). Ones which represent -3, -2, -1, +1, +2, +3 **standard deviation** may be used.

This method indicates clearly which areas are exceptional to the main body of the data. However, one disadvantage of this method is that in normally distributed data it places 68% of all the values in the two categories of +1 and -1 standard deviations.

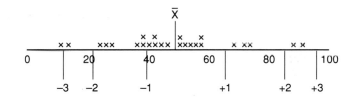

Figure 4.5: Standard deviation classes

5: LINE GRAPHS

When to use

Line graphs are one of the most common ways of displaying results because of this they are often used where other techniques may have been more suitable. The line graph is most effective when displaying continuous measurements, this makes the results sequential. The resulting line will show high and low values as 'peaks' and 'troughs'. It also offers a visual impression of the actual rate of change over time and/or space.

Example

Over time – temperature, air pressure, oxygen/nutrient content of a pond, traffic flows, population changes, farming and/or industrial output.

Method of construction

1 Two axes are drawn (horizontal and vertical).

2 Time intervals are written across the bottom (horizontal axis).

3 The scale for the observed measurements is labelled up the side (vertical axis). This scale does not always have to start at zero, simply choose an appropriate scale that will accurately reflect the nature of your results.

4 Individual points are plotted as small, clear, crosses (x). Use a sharp pencil.

5 Using a ruler and a sharp pencil join up the points in the order they occurred. You can insert more than one set of data (results) on the same axes so long as the scales are identical.

Different colours or different types of line can be used. A number of different types of graph lines are shown in Figure 5.1. The crosses that represent the plotted values must be visible through the graphed line.

A word of caution

These graphs are often used to show or emphasise trends over time, therefore, lines joining individual points can be meaningful (Figures 5.2 and 5.3). However, Figure 5.4 shows one instance where the observed trends may not be meaningful.

Figure 5.1: Suggested graph lines

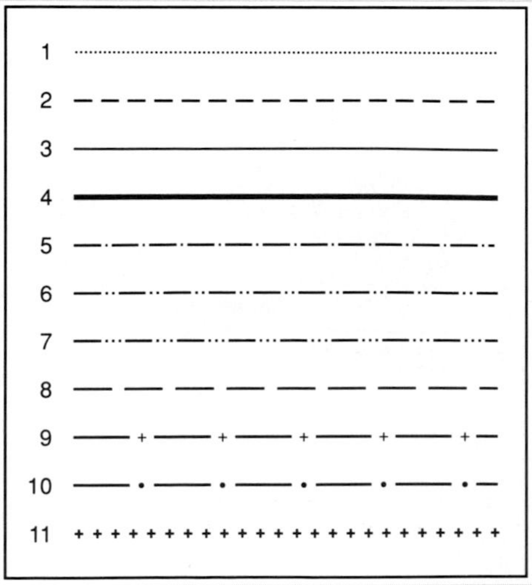

Worked examples

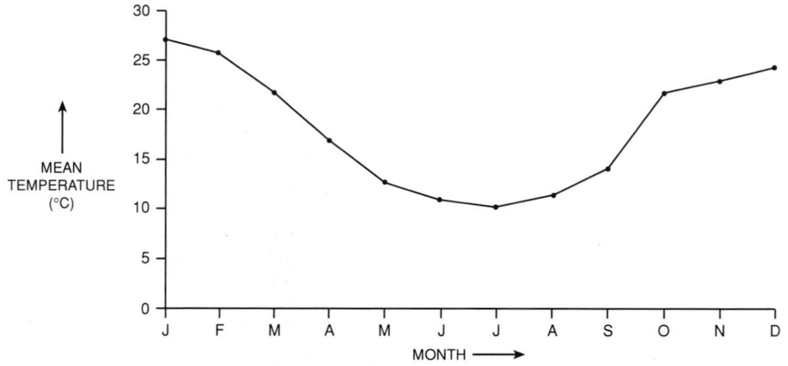

Figure 5.2: Mean monthly temperature for Perth, Australia

Figure 5.3: Population change in Longridge, 1950-80

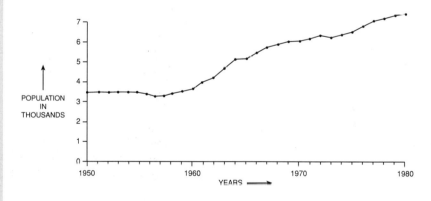

Figure 5.4: Cars sold in Longchester, 1945-59

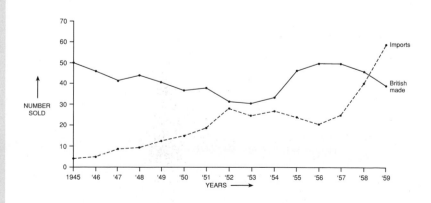

6: PICTOGRAMS

When to use

This involves the use of pictures to show the observed results. Pictograms are visually attractive and should be used when visual attractiveness or appeal is more important than the need for accuracy. They are often used to display information on maps (see the sections on mapping, pages 55-66). Two methods of using pictures are shown in the worked examples below.

Examples

Any data showing change over time or space which can be represented by a single, simple picture – Figures 6.1 and 6.2.

Method of construction

With this particular technique there are two ways of constructing the diagrams. Each has advantages and disadvantages.

Method 1

1   The time/space scale goes up the side (vertical axis).

2   The picture is *drawn* repeatedly across the page. Each picture is the *same size*. The values of the observation is shown by the total number of pictures drawn (Figures 6.1 and 6.4).

3   A key must constructed beforehand and this is then displayed next to the graph.

Worked example

Figure 6.1: Students attending Hothersall Lodge, 1972-76

Method 2

This method is harder to construct because the sizes of pictures for each observation must be worked out.

1   A line (the horizontal axis) is drawn across the page with the time or space scale labelled.

2   A *single picture* is drawn for each observation. The value is indicated by *size* of the picture (Figures 6.2 and 6.5).

3   The number or value is printed above the picture.

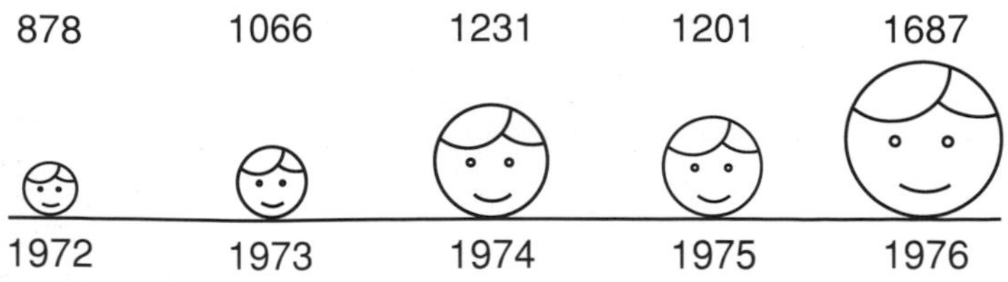

Figure 6.2: Students attending Hothersall Lodge, 1972-76

Worked example

As the observed numbers increase so do the heights of the individual pictures but this does not represent the data you want to display – see previous page.

Problems with this method

Where large numbers of data are involved this method is less accurate than line graphs or bar charts. Furthermore, the second method is not recommended because:

- it is much harder to construct; and
- it can be visually misleading.

For example, if the figures being represented double, the change would be shown by doubling the height of the picture.

To keep the picture in proportion the width of the picture must also be doubled. The picture will now be four times larger to look at and not, as desired, representing a numerically doubled figure (Figure 6.3). It is possible to mathematically overcome this problem – see Section 9: Pie Graphs (pages 26-28).

More worked examples

Figure 6.3: Doubling the height of icons means four times the size

Figure 6.4: Numbers of cars sold in Longchester 1980-85

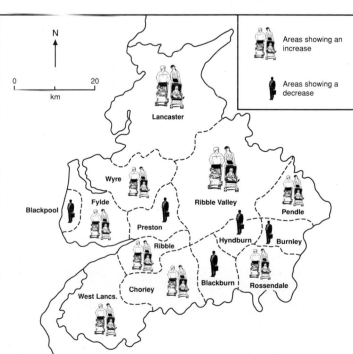

Figure 6.5: Population changes in the districts of Lancashire 1971-81

7: BARCHARTS AND HISTOGRAMS

When to use

Barcharts and histograms are probably the most commonly used ways of presenting fieldwork data. At Hothersall Lodge they have been used to show:

- monthly rainfall totals for one year,
- pebble shape indices distribution within a sediment sample, and
- tree girth and height observations for a single species of tree.

Barcharts and histograms are very similar visually because the data is shown as solid blocks or bars. Despite this there are some very important differences.

Barcharts

These have one quantitative scale – usually the vertical axis – which shows the observed/measured data. This is often called the frequency. The height of each bar reflects the observed frequency. Labels on the horizontal axis show the categories such as place names or the names of fauna and flora.

Histograms

These have two quantitative scales. The vertical scale is the same as the barchart and shows frequency. The horizontal one represents size classes or values, e.g. pebble sizes, age or field size categories. In the case of a histogram it is the area of the block that gives the observed frequency and not necessarily the height. If equal intervals are used across the horizontal axis then this difference loses its importance but this is not always a desirable outcome. The problem of deciding on the size of classes is discussed in greater detail in Section 4: Ways of Classifying Data (pages 14-15). Both types of graph can be displayed on base maps (see the sections on mapping).

Examples

Histograms are best used to display:

- outputs (industrial, agricultural, etc.) from different countries,
- crops grown on a farm or from a region,
- tree type frequencies in a woodland,
- monthly rainfall totals at a given location for one year,
- pebble shape indice distribution within a sediment sample,
- girth and height observations for a single species of tree, and
- number and type of organisms in a river.

The above list indicates that there are many possibilities for using this type of graph, which makes it probably the most commonly used in fieldwork.

Method of construction

1　Draw two axes in the usual way.

2　The observed frequencies are put on the vertical axis. Start at zero and go up at regular intervals. The highest value on the scale should be slightly higher than the largest observed value.

3　The horizontal axis is *either* the different categories in the case of the barchart *or* size class values in the case of the histogram.

4   Label both axes clearly in ink.

5   Using a ruler and pencil draw in the values as rectangles or blocks.

6   Colour or shade in the blocks. Histograms show the frequency distribution of the whole sample and should, therefore, be shaded the same. Barcharts show discrete categories so a different shade/colour should be used for each category.

The worked examples below help to show the important differences between barcharts and histograms. Whichever type of graph you compile make sure your title includes the correct type of name.

Worked examples

Figure 7.1: The results of a quadrat survey carried out on a stretch of open moorland in Yorkshire displayed as a barchart

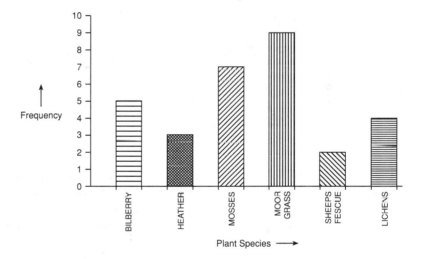

Figure 7.2: The size distribution of 100 pebbles measured on a stretch of mountain stream in North Wales displayed as a histogram

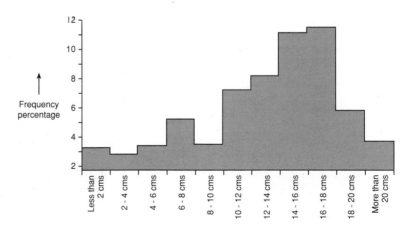

21

The previous section dealt with simple barcharts and histograms, which showed one set of measurements. It is often possible to show more than one set of measurements (observations) on a single barchart and/or histogram. The following examples indicate the range of possibilities.

Pyramids

When to use

These are used when a single set of data is best shown in the form of a pyramid. The same numbers are used to draw blocks/bars on either side of a central axis (Figure 8.1).

Method of construction

1   The different categories should be written in order up the central axis. The order can be very important and must be devised very carefully in advance. For example, Figure 8.1 shows, from the base, primary producers up to the top carnivore.

2   Frequencies/measured values are drawn twice across the bottom (horizontal) scale, one or either side of the central axis. Both start at zero near the centre and go up to a number just higher than the largest measured/observed value.

3   Draw in the blocks/bars then colour/shade the blocks.

The same rules of spacing and shading for barcharts and histograms apply. Figure 8.1 shows spaced bars and a different type of shading for each category, as in a barchart. On a histogram the bars are continuous and shaded the same.

Worked example

Figure 8.1: Population pyramid for a food web in a pond

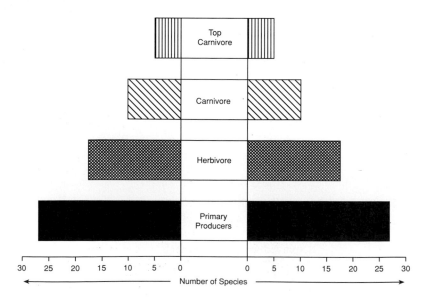

Mirror graphs

These are very similar to the pyramids but they use two sets of measurements/data. The categories are labelled up the central axis; one set of data is drawn on the left of this and the second set is drawn on the right (Figure 8.2).

Mirror graphs are ideal for comparing/contrasting two sets of data collected at different locations. Once again the ordering of the categories up the central axis is important. If organised properly mirror graphs can be visually attractive.

Examples

Can be used to record pebble sizes or roundness at two different sites on a river; population pyramids (male and female treated separately); land use sampled at two different locations (highland and lowland).

Figure 8.2: Vegetation survey on a podsol and a peat soil (Bowland)

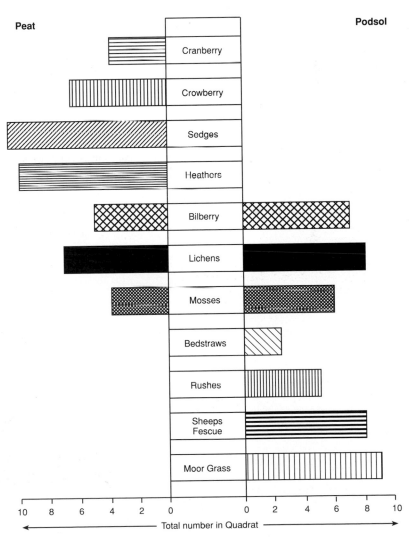

Mirror graphs are also based on barcharts and if you can use colours to shade in the categories this produces a better visual result than the shading used in Figure 8.2.

Multiple bar charts/histograms

These are usually used where three or four sets of data which have the same categories are to be displayed on one graph. If you have two sets of data use a mirrorgraph as above. If you have more than four sets of data draw separate graphs for each one, otherwise multiple barcharts start to become complicated.

Each category will have several bars/blocks representing the different sets of data. The height of the bar indicates the value of each category. The horizontal scale is for the categories and the vertical scale is for the observed/measured values. Each set of data has a different shading or colour. Figures 8.3 and 8.4 should make this clear.

Worked examples

As the data in Figure 8.3 is continuous the categories are joined together as for a histogram. Had the information been intended for a barchart a small gap would be placed between each of the categories (classes). Figure 8.4 shows this sort of arrangement.

Figure 8.3: Stone survey at three locations along the long profile of a stream

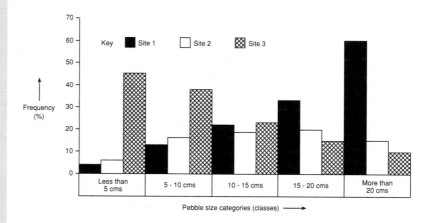

Figure 8.4: Cars sold in town 'A', 1972-76

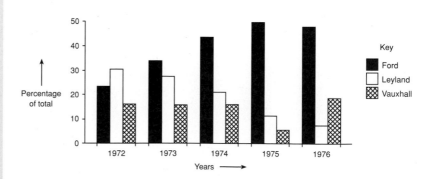

24

Composite barcharts

This type of graph is usually used with barchart-type data. Histogram data can sometimes be adapted and used but it is less common to do so. The rules on using this type of graph are different from those governing multiple barcharts. With composite barcharts any number of sets of data can be shown on the graph. However, there should be no more than four or five different component categories within each of these sets of data.

Method of construction

There are two ways of drawing composite barcharts.

Method 1

Each set of data is shown on the same graph as a single bar or block. The six sets of data equal six bars on the graph. The height of the bars represent the actual totals of each set of data, therefore, changes in the totals can be seen as changes in the length of the bars. The bars are then sub-divided into the different component categories (Figure 8.5).

Method 2

If the total sizes are unimportant then the component categories of each set of data can be converted to a percentage of the whole. Each of the bars is drawn the same size (Figure 8.6), making a comparison of the different component categories more accurate and easier than in Method 1 above.

Figures 8.5 and 8.6 show how graphs drawn (using the same data as for Figure 8.4) using Methods 1 and 2 respectively will appear. Table 1 in Appendix 1 indicates how the percentages for Figure 8.6 were calculated.

Worked examples

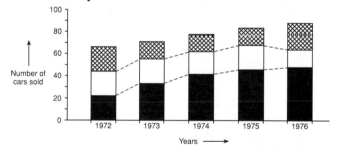

Figure 8.5: Cars sold in town 'A', 1972-76

Figure 8.5 shows the total changes from year to year, however, it is not easy to interpret changes in the component categories, i.e. the makes of car. When you require this type of information use a percentage composite barchart as shown in Figure 8.6.

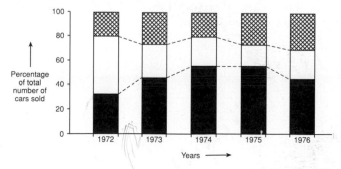

Figure 8.6: Percentage of total number of cars sold in town 'A', 1972-76

9: PIE GRAPHS

When to use

A pie graph is a circle divided into sections rather like the slices of a cake or pie. These sections are called the component categories. A finished pie graph gives a good impression of the different component categories and the relative proportions that go to make up the total, i.e. the complete circle.

Pie graphs are best used when there are four or more categories involved which, as we have seen, tends to be too many for composite and multiple barcharts (pages 24 and 25). They are often used to compare two or more sets of data. And, if you intend to do so *be warned* pie graphs with more than five or six component categories become difficult to interpret.

Pie graphs are commonly used to display results on base maps (see pages 58-60).

Examples
Any sample that can be divided up into definite component categories – land use, vegetation surveys, traffic counts, housing ages and styles.

The particular method depends on the nature of the data you wish to display. There are a few basic rules to the construction of pie graphs:

1 If the size of the different samples is different use proportional circles (see page 58), e.g. traffic counted at three sample points gave totals of 23, 45 and 13 vehicles.

2 If the sizes of the different samples are the same or the component categories are to be expressed as a percentage of the total use equal sized circles, i.e. each circle has the same radius.

Proportional circles
The area of the circle must represent the total sample size. Choose an appropriate scale for the radius, e.g. 1cm = 10 vehicles/fields/people. You must now work out the radius for all the samples.

To calculate the length of the radii work out the following:

• the radius using the original scale (1cm = 10 vehicles);
• the square root of this length.

This will be the radius length you require to draw your circle. Table 9.1 shows the calculation for our particular example.

Note: The length of the radius for each circle is not directly related to the sample size. For example, two samples are to be shown as two pie graphs. There are 20 units in the first sample and 40 in the second and, because of this the area of the second circle must be double the area of the first. This doubling of the area is not brought about by doubling the radius. Therefore the area of a circle is πr^2 and not πr.

Table 9.1

Sample number	Total in sample	Radius using scale (1cm = 10 vehicles)	Square root (radius length drawn in cm)
1	20	2.0	1.41
2	40	4.0	2.00

This example indicates that a doubling in sample size does not give a doubling in the radius length (1.41cm and 2.0cm).

Another alternative is to construct an accurate scale line – see Section 17: Proportional Symbols page 58. In practice the use of a scale line is only worth the effort when you have large numbers of circles to construct. This is often the case when they are used on base maps (see pages 58-60). For method of construction see below.

Equal sized circles

These are used when sample sizes are identical or the component categories are to be expressed as a percentage of the whole. Use a simple scale for the desired circle size and all your circles should use the same radius length.

Method of construction

Once the circles have been drawn the following steps are followed for *both* proportional circles and equal sized circles.

1   Each circle can now be divided into its component categories. A little mathematics is involved in converting the observed frequencies into angles which can then be used to divide up the circle from the centre. The equation required for the calculation uses the same principle as for percentages (Equation 9.1).

Equation 9.1

$$\text{Angle of component category} = \frac{\text{Observed category size}}{\text{Total sample size}} \times 360$$

Table 9.2 shows how the angles have been worked out for Figure 9.1.

Category name	Category size	$\frac{\text{Category size}}{\text{total size}} \times 360 =$	Angle on pie graph
Cars	27	27/40 x 360 =	243°
Lorries	5	5/40 x 360 =	45°
Vans	3	3/40 x 360 =	27°
Buses	2	2/40 x 360 =	18°
Others	3	3/40 x 360 =	27°
Total size	40	40/40 x 360 =	360°

Table 9.2: Vehicles passing along Water Street, Chipping, 12 November 1987 (12.00-12.30p.m.)

An alternative method would be to find the angle corresponding to one item – in this case 1 vehicle (see Equation 9.2).

$$\text{Angle for 1 vehicle} = \frac{1}{40} \times 360 = 9°$$

The maths is now very simple, for example 5 lorries = 5 x 9 = 45°

Equation 9.2

2   Using a protractor divide the circle by using angles at the centre and work clockwise adding each category. So the first category is placed to the right of 12 noon. If you have a 'miscellaneous' or 'others' category this goes on last (immediately anti-clockwise of 12 noon). Where more than one pie graph is drawn the categories must appear in the same order.

3   Colour or shade the different sections. Where you have more than one pie graph use the same colour/shading for each of the component categories. Add labels in ink and do not forget to include a key.

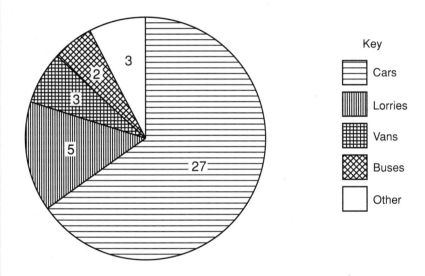

Figure 9.1: Vehicles passing along Water Street, Chipping, 12 November 1987 (12.00-12.30p.m.) using data from Table 9.2

28

10: SCATTERGRAPHS (CORRELATION GRAPHS)

When to use

Most of the graphs described in previous sections have single types of observation/measurement, for example, pebble size, numbers of vehicles. Scattergraphs use two different types of observation called *variables*. Scattergraphs are used to show graphically any connection/relationship between the two variables (another name for connection is **correlation** hence 'correlation graph'). Scattergraphs are one of the most commonly used types of graph.

Examples

Because geographical enquiries are often concerned with the connection between paired variables there are literally hundreds of cases where this type of graph might be used. For example, air temperature and altitude, slope angle and soil depth, building age with distance from a CBD.

Method of construction

Here we use altitude against air temperature as an example.

1 Two axes are drawn in the usual way with both scales just exceeding the highest recorded value. Try to decide which variable is causing the change in the other. This is called the *independent variable* and occupies the horizontal axis. The variable being changed by this is called the *dependent variable* and occupies the vertical axis. In our example, altitude is the independent variable and air temperature is the dependent variable.

2 Plot each *pair* of figures as a single point using the observed data as co-ordinates. The more points (paired data) the more reliable the graph. *Do not join up these points.*

3 Study the resulting pattern. The possible patterns are explained in 'Scattergraph patterns' on pages 31-32, these will help you analyse your graph. You may be able to add a 'Line of best fit' using a sharp pencil and ruler. Try to draw in, by eye, a straight line, it should appear to pass as close as possible to all the points plotted. This is not possible if your graph shows little or no correlation. The line does not need to pass through the point of origin (where the two axes meet).

4 If you can include a line of best fit then predictions of unknown values can be made. In Figure 10.1 the predicted temperature at 250m is 15°C. The line of best fit also highlights any 'rogue points' or anomalies in the data. These can then be traced to source and investigated further.

Note: The line of best fit can be drawn onto the graph accurately using a statistical test called regression but to do this you will need a good statistics manual – see the companion manual *Methods of Statistical Analysis of Fieldwork Data.*

Worked example

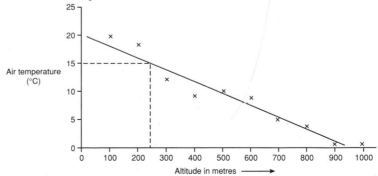

Figure 10.1: What is the connection between altitude and air temperature?

A scattergraph variation

The scattergraph method (described above) is used to show a relationship or connection between two variables that have been expressed quantitatively. It is equally possible to use a similar method to show the connection between two variables where only one of the variables has a quantitative value, the second variable having a non-quantitative value (land use, geology, soil type, etc.).

Examples

Any two connected variables where one has a non-quantitative value:

Land use		Altitude
Vegetation type		Gradient
Rock type	**against**	Soil variables (e.g. soil pH)
Soil type		

Building materials		Distance
Building functions	**against**	from
Environmental factors		CBD

Method of construction

Here we use the example of land use against altitude.

1 Draw your two axes in the usual way.

2 The quantitative variable (altitude) usually uses the vertical axis and is labelled as for any other numerical scale.

3 The non-quantitative variable (type of land use) uses the horizontal scale. Each of the different land use types is allocated a 'block' of equal width. The order across the scale may be important, for example, if there is a preconceived idea **(hypothesis)** as to the expected connection between land use and altitude then the categories may be placed in the anticipated order.

4 The observed values are plotted in a similar manner to scattergraphs (see Figure 10.2).

5 It is not usual to try to include a line of best fit, rather 'zones' and 'overall trends' are identified. Our example shows the altitude zones of each type of land use, its upper and lower limits, merging boundaries, and patterns of land use with an increase in height.

Note: All types of scattergraphs appear, at first sight, to be very useful when it comes to hypothesis testing, especially where correlations are involved, but they must be treated with care. Read 'Scattergraph patterns' carefully.

Worked example

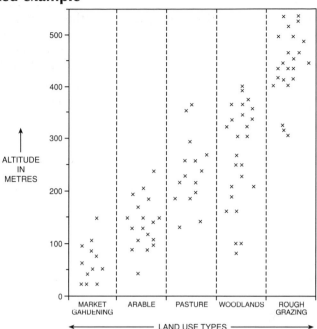

Figure 10.2: Is there any correlation between altitude and land use?

Scattergraph patterns

Here the closer the points are to a single straight line the better the correlation (connection) between the two variables. Figures 10.3 to 10.8 and their accompanying explanations indicate what some patterns may mean.

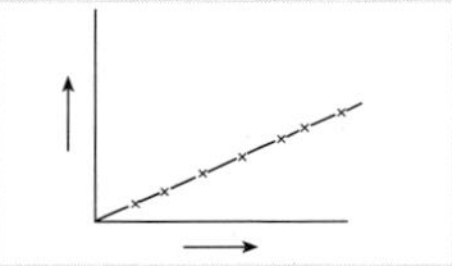

Perfect correlation

All points lie on the line of best fit. In this case the correlation is a positive one, however, this rule applies equally applies to negative correlations. (A correlation of either +1.0 or -1.0). You cannot get a better connection between any two variables than this.

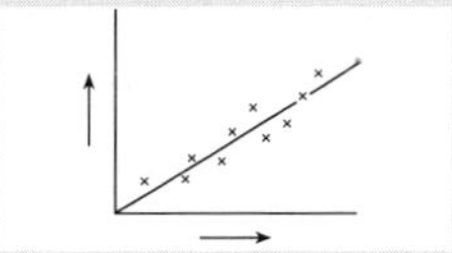

Positive correlation

Not a perfect correlation but, because the points are close to the line of best fit, a positive correlation. In a positive correlation, as one of the variables increases in size so does the other, e.g. wind speed and altitude, stream order, discharge, cross sectional area with distance downstream.

Negative correlation

Similar to the previous graph except as one variable increases in size the other decreases, e.g. air temperature and altitude, stone size with distance downstream.

The three examples above show some form of correlation between the two sets of variables. Not all the graphs you draw will look like these so here are two more examples of what a graph looks like when there is little or no correlation.

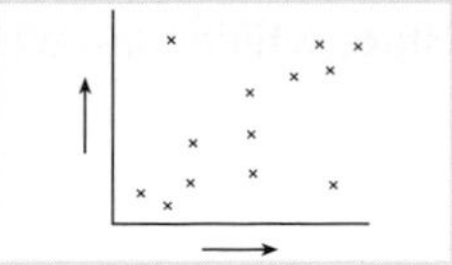

Poor correlation

With a poor correlation there is some sort of connection but the points are some distance from a straight line. In this case it is difficult to insert a line of best fit. Graphs showing these sorts of results are inconclusive and more data needs to be collected.

Figure 10.3:
Perfect correlation

Figure 10.4:
Positive correlation

Figure 10.5:
Negative correlation

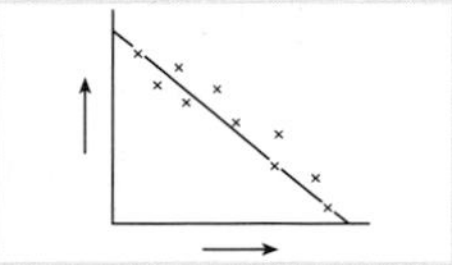

Figure 10.6:
Poor correlation

Figure 10.7:
No correlation

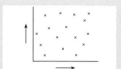

No correlation
Here the points appear at random on the graph and there is no real straight line pattern. The results show that there is no connection (no correlation) between the two variables.

Warning: Scattergraphs have limitations

1 It is often difficult to put on a line of best fit by eye. The regression analysis is much more accurate but can be complex.

2 Not all correlations between variables are straight lines (linear). Some appear as curves which makes the fitting of a regression line difficult. Figure 10.8 illustrates such a relationship.

The answer to this problem may be to plot the results either using the logarithmic values of the data or by graphing on logarithmic paper (see pages 41-43).

Figure 10.8: Non-linear correlation

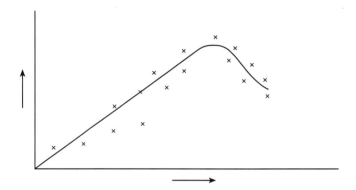

3 What might appear to be a strong correlation does not always imply that one variable has influenced the other because:

a the resulting graph may have been caused by chance. By experimenting with various pairs of data it is often possible to get a 'nonsense conclusion'. Statistics can be misleading, for instance, two sets of variables may appear to give a good correlation even though the two variables could never be connected. It is possible to show that the birth rate in Sweden changes directly with the number of stork nesting sites!

b the correlation is caused by a *third variable* that has not been considered. For instance, a temperature decrease which may appear to be related to a rise in altitude may be caused by a third variable, i.e. wind speed.

Worked examples

Each of the following graphs (Figures 10.9 to 10.11) shows a different type of correlation. Can your students say what type each graph is, how close the connections are, and explain the patterns in each graph. They should also be able to state which variables are independent and which dependent.

Note: Use and analyse scatter-graphs with extreme care as they can be misleading.

Figure 10.9: Pedestrian densities with distance from the peak land value site of an urban CBD

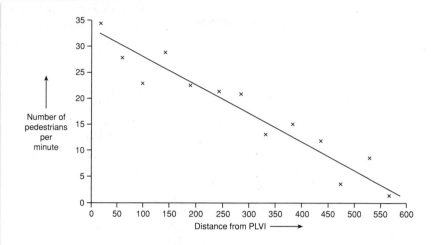

Figure 10.10: River discharge with distance downstream from the source

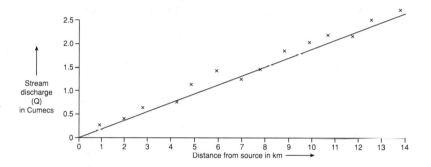

Figure 10.11: Students in a class were asked how many relatives they had and were then given a test in mathematics

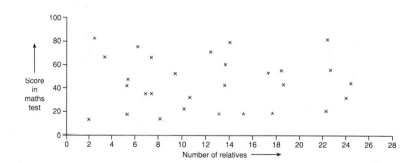

When to use

Rose diagrams (often called Star diagrams) are used when the observed data takes the form of a compass direction or bearing. The end result is a visual impression of any predominant **orientation** that the data may display. You can then test the significance of this orientation statistically using either a Vector analysis or a Chi squared (χ^2) test (see *Methods of Statistical Analysis of Fieldwork Data*).

Examples

Rose diagrams are best used when you wish to display predominant wind directions and strengths. Sediment analysis (orientation of fluvial, marine, glacial, talus deposits), or the morphometric analysis of such features as drumlins, corries, shakeholes, may use **azimuths.**

Method of construction

The way you choose to construct a rose diagram usually depends on the nature and complexity of your data. In nearly all cases the data must be put into pre-arranged categories, for example, north, north-east, east, or bearings of 0-9°, 10-19°, 20-29°. The most commonly used methods are shown in this section together with worked examples.

Simple roses

Take your compass direction either over a given time or for a particular sample size. For the simplest type of rose you should put these directions into categories which represent the eight points of the compass. All arms should be drawn to the same width, but you must work out a scale for the length of the arm, the length of the arm should show the frequency (Figure 11.1).

Worked example

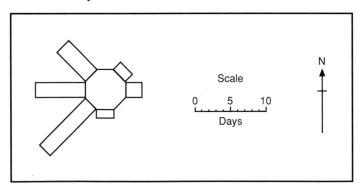

Figure 11.1: Wind directions observed at Hothersall Lodge field study centre over a period of one month

If you wish to be more precise use 16 compass points or even size classes (0-9°, 10-19°, 20-29°, etc). This method is discussed in greater detail below.

Compound roses

It is possible to display several variables on one graph or compound rose. For example, you may wish to show wind direction, frequency and strength (Figure 11.2). Again the length of the bar represents frequency but on compound roses the width of the bar represents wind speed/strength. In this particular case (Figure 11.2) the number of categories available is restricted by the inclusion of the second variable: wind speed.

Worked example

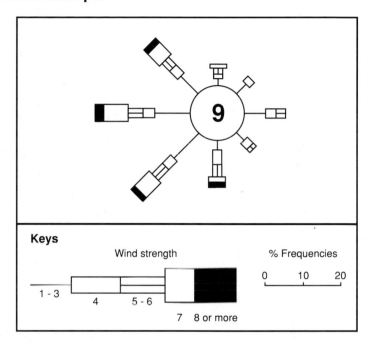

Figure 11.2: Wind direction and strength observed at Hothersall Lodge for 1984. Notes: (i) the length of each line represents the percentage frequency of each wind direction, (ii) wind strengths are from the Beaufort scale (shown in the key), and (iii) the number in the circle represents the percentage frequency of calms.

Azimuths

An azimuth is a compass bearing and these are commonly used when sediment or morphological orientations are to be displayed The 'raw' data is collected in the field as an exact compass bearing. This is then categorised into classes, for example 0-9°, 10-19°. These classes are called **azimuthal classes.** (Using a table to show azimuthal class and frequency is useful at this stage.) The class interval chosen is important, if it is too large, e.g. every 40° or 50°, the resulting patterns are not a true reflection of reality. However, if the classes are too small then patterns (preferred orientation) may not appear even if they actually exist in reality. Sample size is equally important the larger the sample the better the resulting azimuth.

Method of construction

Once the data has been categorised the graphs can then be drawn as follows:

1   A straight line is plotted along the mid point of each azimuthal class, e.g. the *mid point* of the azimuthal class 20-29° is 24.5. The length of the line is, therefore, related to the frequency of each class.

2 The lines may be dealt with in three ways, they can be: (i) left as single lines as in Figure 11.3(a), (ii) the end can be connected together and shaded as in Figure 11.3(b), or (iii) each azimuthal class is shaded up to the end of the line as in Figure 11.3(c). In practice the third method is most commonly adopted. Concentric circles are included on Figure 11.3 to give an idea of frequency.

Worked example

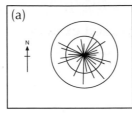 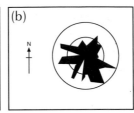 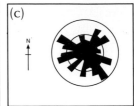

Figure 11.3: Example azimuths

Reflected, half and single roses

With some data each feature has two opposite bearings, e.g. the long axis of a drumlin may be 10° and 190°. Other examples are the axes of sediments, shakeholes, roads and streets. The resulting rose must show two reflected/mirrored halves (Figure 11.4(a)). Many fieldworkers construct only half the rose (0-180°) when this data is involved (Figure 11.4(b)).

For some sets of data only a single bearing is possible, e.g. wind direction, corrie orientation. In these particular cases a full rose (0-359°) is constructed – see Figure 11.5.

Worked examples

Figure 11.4 shows the long axis orientation of bedload in an upland stream. The arrow indicates the direction of water flow.

Note: Single rose diagrams are valid only if a large sample is involved.

Figure 11.4: (a) reflected, and (b) half rose (using same data)

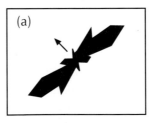 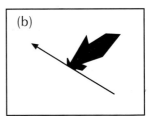

Figure 11.5: Single wind rose for 1962-66

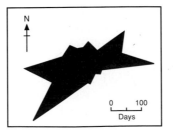

Some types of graph have a limited application but are well worth a mention.

Triangular graphs

These are sometimes called *ternary diagrams* and have three axes instead of two. They take the form of an equilateral triangle (Figure 12.1). The important features of triangular graphs are:

1 Each axis is divided into 100 – representing percentages.

2 From each axis lines are drawn at an angle of 60° to carry the values across the graph.

3 The data must be in the form of three components, each one representing a percentage value and these values must add up to 100.

The main value of triangular graphs arises when data for several locations is plotted on one graph. The relative position of the points offers a quick visual impression of the dominance of one component or another. Triangular graphs can be confusing at first acquaintance, so care must be taken when plotting and interpreting them.

Examples

Triangular graphs can be used to show employment structure (primary, secondary and tertiary) (see, e.g. Figure 12.2), soil particle size (silt, clay and sand), agricultural land use (arable, pastoral, others), etc.

Worked example

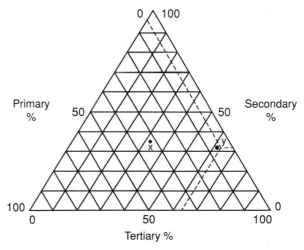

PRIMARY	5%
SECONDARY	33%
TERTIARY	62%

Figure 12.1: Basic triangular graph indicating the way in which the values are carried across the graph

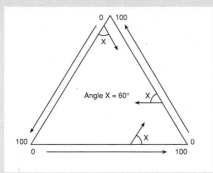

Figure 12.2: Employment structure of a county. X marks the point where all three elements are identical

Circular graphs

These are sometimes used to show a variable that is continuous over time, such as temperature data. Whereas on a normal line graph there is a false break, for example, if data starts on 1 January and ends on 31 December, on a circular graph this break does not occur (see Figure 12.3).

Circular graphs are easy to draw. They have two axes – the circumference of the circle usually represents time (e.g. months of the year – Figures 12.3 and 12.4) and the radius which represents the observed values (e.g. temperature, oxygen content of a pond).

The main drawback to using circular graphs is that the change over time is shown by the line's relative position to the centre of the circle. This makes the interpretation more difficult than the straightforward rises and falls of a line graph. However, with increasing familiarity your students will increase their competence in interpretation.

Examples
Yearly temperature and air pressure readings, yearly variables of a pond, traffic flows, or any other continuous variable over a time period.

Worked examples

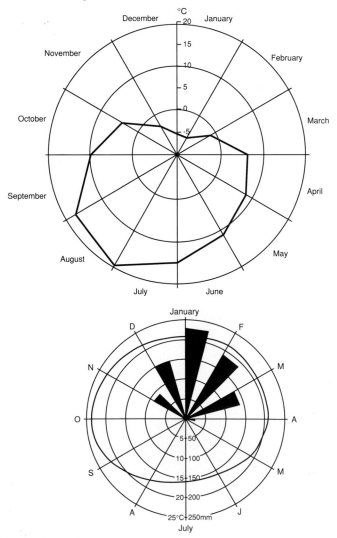

Figure 12.3: Average monthly temperatures for Moscow, Russia

Figure 12.4: Average monthly temperature and rainfall for Lusaka, Zambia. Source: Frost, 1985

Polar co-ordinates

Polar co-ordinate graphs are related to rose diagrams and scattergraphs, both of which have been described in earlier sections. In many cases polar co-ordinate graphs are actually referred to as the scattergraph equivalent of rose diagrams.

In appearance polar co-ordinates are rather similar to circular graphs, however, there are three very important differences between the two.

1 Scattergraphs include two variables, one of which is always **orientation.** This is expressed as a compass bearing from north (as is the case with rose diagrams).
2 The second variable is represented by the distance from the centre of the graph. This can represent any variable quantity, e.g. size, altitude.
3 In polar co-ordinates a third dimension may be introduced either by varying the size of the symbol used (dot, cross, etc.), to show abundance or by the use of different symbols for different categories of observation (Figure 12.5).

Furthermore, a polar co-ordinate is a specialised type of graph and can only be used where the data shows some form of orientation as one of its variables.

Examples

Examples may include: *corries* – aspect against altitude, aspect against size; *vegetation types* – aspect of slope against gradient against frequency of occurrence; *slopes* – aspect against any soil variable (pH, water, humus content, etc.).

Worked example

Figure 12.5: Corrie orientation against altitude in North Wales

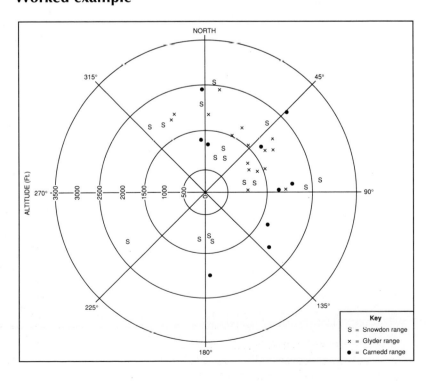

Figure 12.5 shows the orientation of corries in North Wales against their altitude. The corries have been divided into the three main mountain ranges included in the survey. These are indicated by using three different symbols.

Reverse bars

Reverse bar graphs are related in appearance and method of construction to barcharts and histograms. They are commonly used when negative values as well as positive values are represented. As Figures 12.6 and 12.7 indicate, reverse bar graphs are especially useful when you want to show trends/changes over time and/or space.

Method of construction

This is fairly straightforward. The horizontal axis represents the categories involved whilst the vertical axis is drawn above and below the end of the horizontal axis (Figure 12.6). Values above the horizontal are positive and those ranging below the horizontal are negative. Figure 12.7 indicates how effectively this particular type of graph can be used on base maps.

Worked examples

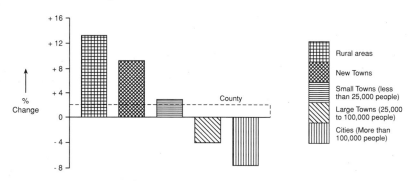

Figure 12.6: Population changes in Lancashire's urban and rural area, 1971-81

Figure 12.7: Population changes in selected age groups, Lancashire districts, 1971-81

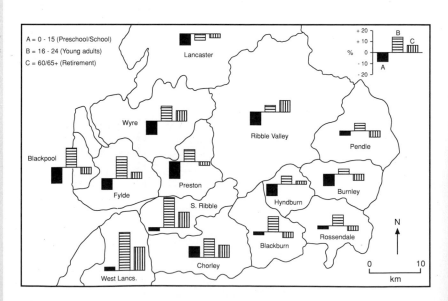

13: LOGARITHMIC GRAPHS

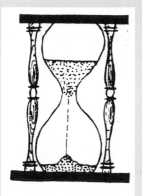

When to use

Logarithmic graphs can provide a useful tool for displaying and analysing some types of fieldwork data. The values can be plotted directly onto logarithmic graph paper or the logarithmic values of the raw data can be plotted onto normal (arithmetic) graph paper. Both methods are illustrated below.

There are several valid applications of this technique although only the two main situations in which the use of logarithmic graphs is helpful are shown here.

1   When the range of values of one or both of the scales is so large that a meaningful graph cannot be plotted onto a sheet of linear scale graph paper.

2   Where the purpose of the data collection is to compare rates of growth of variables.

Examples

Logarithmic graphs are most useful for the representation of economic data, changes in population size, agricultural yields, energy production, graphs where the rates of increase or decrease are compared.

Method of construction

As mentioned above specially printed logarithmic paper may be used (this is available from good stationers). Alternatively, the logarithmic values of the data may be plotted onto arithmetic graph paper. If your students use a pocket calculator they should find this technique simple and straightforward.

Types of logarithmic paper

There are essentially two types of logarithmic paper. Figure 13.1(a) shows paper with one logarithmic and one linear scale (semi-log or log/linear paper). Figure 13.1(b) shows paper with two logarithmic scales (log/log paper).

Figure 13.1(a): Log/linear graph paper (three cycles), **(b)** Log/log graph paper (two cycles)

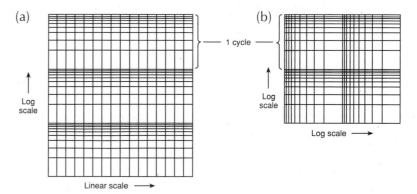

Worked examples

The values for population growth of towns A, B and C, obtained from census material, is shown in Table 13.1. The aim of the data collection is to compare the growth rate of each town.

Town	1900	1910	1920	1930	1940	1950	1960	1970	1980
A	3000	4000	5200	6800	8900	11 500	15 000	20 000	26 000
B	8100	10 500	18 500	24 000	24 000	31 500	41 000	54 000	70 000
C	80 000	87 000	94 000	104 000	112 000	121 000	133 000	145 000	158 000

Table 13.1: Population figures for three towns: A, B and C, 1900-1980

One advantage of displaying the population of each town on the same graph is that visual comparisons are possible. However, the values (from 3000 to 158 000) are dispersed over too wide a range for a meaningful linear graph to be constructed. The size of the graph would become too cumbersome or its scale so reduced that the line plotted for town A would be quite inaccurate. In this case log/linear paper is a more useful tool.

1 The first decision you must make is where to set a base line. A logarithmic graph does not include zero, with each diminishing cycle the values decrease but never actually reach nought. Convenient base lines are to the power of ten, e.g. 0.1, 1, 10, 100, 1000, 10 000. Choose one immediately below the lowest value in your table. In Table 13.1 the lowest value is 3000, hence the most convenient base line is 1000.

2 Next insert the scales. In our example the X axis is a conventional linear scale and is used to represent time (years). The Y axis is divided into a series of cycles or decades, each cycle represents a multiple of ten. Therefore, with a base line of 1000 our next cycle begins at 10 000 and the third at 100 000. For our range of values three cycle paper is adequate, although for greater ranges paper with more cycles is available. Six cycle paper would allow a range of values from 1 to 1 million.

3 Finally, you should plot the values directly onto the paper.

There is one further advantage of employing logarithmic graphs (in addition to allowing us to plot a wide range of figures) they actually indicate the rate of change. So here the inclination of each plotted line indicates that towns A and B have identical growth rates which are both higher than town C. This fact is not immediately obvious from examining the data alone.

In certain cases it is advantageous to use graph paper with two logarithmic scales, for example, when both variables exhibit a wide range of values or when confidence limit lines are required on a divergent scattergraph. (The latter is outside the scope of this book and reference to more advanced statistical texts is advised.) The construction of a graph with two logarithmic scales is the same as the construction of the logarithmic scale of Figure 13.3.

Figure 13.3: Log/linear graph showing the population increase of towns A, B and C, 1900-80

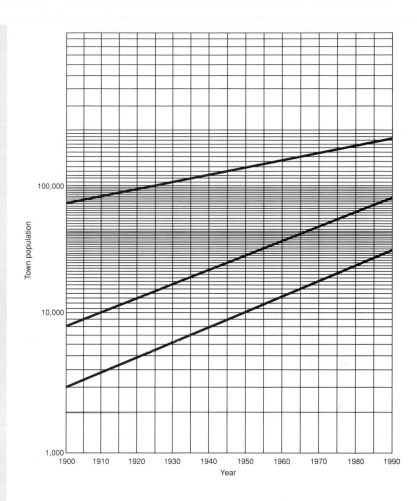

14: PROFILES AND CROSS SECTIONS

Note: If you are drawing more than one profile use the same scale throughout.

One necessary skill all students should have is the ability to construct accurate side views (profiles or cross sections) of geographical features such as river channels and beach profiles. Several profiles or cross section can be displayed together to indicate changes in shape and size from one location to the next. In addition, profiles or cross sections are often used as base diagrams for displaying other related data, for example, stream velocities across a stretch of a river meander, pebble sizes and shapes along a beach. Cross sections are frequently used to accurately calculate areas. By combining these diagrams with other measurements volumes can be calculated, for example, grike sizes on limestone pavement.

Examples
Profiles – slopes, valleys, beaches, corries, waterfalls, etc.
Cross sections – river channels, gullies, limestone pavements.

Even though they appear similar, there are important differences between profiles and cross sections, because of the differences they are dealt with in separate sections below.

Profiles
Data to compile profiles is usually collected by one of two methods:

1   Divide the feature into separate, definite, straight sections and take measurements of gradient and length for each section.

2   Take an accurate gradient measurement at regular intervals, for example, every metre. Either by using a pantometer or by accurate surveying techniques.

Method of construction
1   Work out the total length of the profile to be drawn.

2   Calculate a suitable scale so that the drawn profile will fit neatly onto your graph paper. Remember, because of the angles, once the profile is drawn the total length will be 'dragged in'.

3   Start at one end of the profile. Draw in the first set of measurements using a protractor for the angle and a ruler and scale for the length.

4   Work your way along the profile in the same manner until it is complete.

The profile in Figure 14.1 shows the shape of the slope. Its accompanying table records some of the variables measured in each section. After drawing up profiles like this you could construct scattergrams to see if any connections/correlations occur between these variables.

Worked example

Scale: 2 millimetres = 1 metre

LENGTHS (m)	7	16	10	8	11	21
ANGLES (°)		5	12	65	4	-3

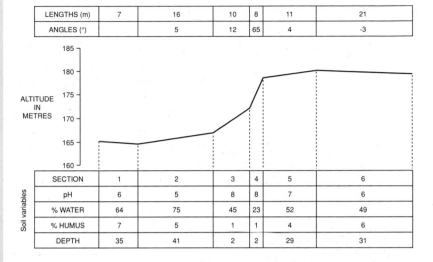

ALTITUDE IN METRES

Soil variables

SECTION	1	2	3	4	5	6
pH	6	5	8	8	7	6
% WATER	64	75	45	23	52	49
% HUMUS	7	5	1	1	4	6
DEPTH	35	41	2	2	29	31

Cross sections

These are usually constructed by measuring the width of the feature and then taking depth/height measurements at regular intervals across this width. The greater the number of measurements the more accurate the finished cross section.

Method of construction

Cross sections require both vertical and horizontal scales. If possible the scales should be identical (Figure 14.2), however, where the shape of the feature is shallow (e.g. a small stream) you may need to exaggerate the vertical scale to make it more easily readable (Figure 14.3). Be warned you will encounter problems if you need to use the resulting exaggerated cross section for further calculations, e.g. wetted perimeter, hydraulic radius. This problem is discussed in greater detail in this section.

1 Take the width of the feature and calculate a scale which allows the width to fit comfortably onto your graph paper. This is the horizontal scale. Draw a line across the page to represent the width.

2 On this horizontal scale mark off the intervals at which you took the height/depth measurements.

3 Work out a suitable vertical scale. Does it have to be exaggerated and, if so, by how much? Construct a scale line to the left of the horizontal width line and label depth/height measurements according to your vertical scale.

4 Using the width interval points and your vertical scale line mark off the depth/height measurements as small, neat, pencil crosses.

5 Join up these crosses by hand, not with a ruler, because in reality these sections are rarely regular straight lines.

Note: If you are drawing more than one section, e.g. for comparison, make sure that the horizontal scale and the vertical scale stay the same throughout.

Figure 14.2: Cross section of a small stream channel: (a) horizontal and vertical scale identical – 1m = 1cm, and (b) horizontal scale identical to (a) above and vertical scale exaggerated by 5 – i.e. 1m = 5cm

Worked example

For this example depth measurements were taken at 1m intervals across the stream.

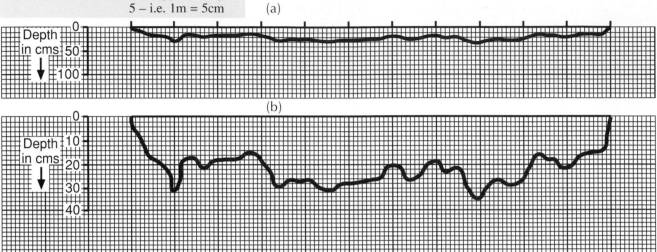

Using cross sections for further calculations

It is possible to use accurately constructed cross sections to work out other characteristics of the feature you are studying. Some of these calculations can be made where you have used an exaggerated vertical scale, others cannot.

Cross sectional area (CSA)

This is an important calculation because it is often used as an indicator of size and is an integral part of the calculation of river discharges (Q).

The simplest method of calculating the CSA is by counting the squares that appear inside the actual cross section on your graph paper. On Figure 14.2(a) the two scales are identical so there are less squares to count, however, it is more accurate to use Figure 14.2(b) where the vertical scale is exaggerated by five. The reason for this is that the error caused by estimating fractions of those squares not fully inside the channel (i.e. on either side of the line) is greatly minimised with an exaggeration of the vertical scale.

Method of construction

1 Count up the number of squares on the graph paper. In the case of Figure 14.2(b) there are 938 1mm squares.

2 Divide this total by the number of times the vertical scale has been exaggerated – in this case five – Equation 14.3:

Equation 14.3

$$\frac{938}{5} = 187.6$$

If we count the squares where the two scales are identical in (Figure 14.2(a)) we get the same answer, i.e. 187.6.

3 The scale 1cm = 1m means that each 1mm square on the graph represents 0.01sq m in reality. To obtain the cross sectional area in square metres multiply the number of squares (187.6) by 0.01 (Equation 14.4).

Equation 14.4

187.6 x 0.01 = 1.876 sq m

Wetted perimeter (WP)

In the previous calculations the exaggerated vertical scale did not present problems because the total is divided by the degree of exaggeration. If, however, you want to calculate the wetted perimeter (i.e. that part of the channel that is in contact with the stream, bed and bank) you *must use the same scale for the vertical and the horizontal axes.*

Method of construction

1 Use either a fine piece of string or a pair of dividers to measure the length of the channel that is in contact with the water. This was done using Figure 14.2(a).

Wetted perimeter on cross section = 10.2cm
Wetted perimeter in reality = 10.2m.

Hydraulic radius

We can now use the cross sectional area and the wetted perimeter to calculate the efficiency of the channel (Equation 14.4.). This is often called the hydraulic radius (HR).

Equation 14.4

$$\text{Hydraulic radius} = \frac{\text{Cross sectional area}}{\text{Wetted perimeter}}$$

The figures already calculated are then used to work out the efficiency of the channel used in Figure 14.2 (Equation 14.5).

Equation 14.5

$$HR = \frac{1.876}{10.200} = 0.164$$

The higher the hydraulic radius the greater the efficiency of the channel to minimise friction between the channel and stream flow. This particular example has a poor efficiency which is what we would expect from such a shape.

Summary

The decision of whether to exaggerate the vertical scale depends on what you need the cross section for in the first place. These may be summarised as:

1 exaggerate the scale if you are either interested in observing the shape of shallow features, using it as a base for displaying other observed measurements or for accurate calculations of the cross sectional areas of a small/shallow stream;

47

2 use identical scales if the feature is large or if you want to calculate the wetted perimeter or the hydraulic radius.

You may find it useful to draw both types for each set of data.

Using profiles/cross sections as a base for displaying other results

This is particularly useful when *transects* of one form or another are carried out. For these measurements are taken at regular intervals across the feature (see also Section 15: Transects – pages 49-54). Examples of how profiles and cross sections can be used to display this type of material are shown in Figures 14.4 and 14.5.

Worked examples

Figure 14.4: Transect showing vegetation change up a slope

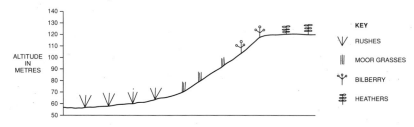

For this example (Figure 14.5) 100 pebbles were sampled at three sites across a meander these were allocated to size classes. Histograms were constructed on the cross section of the meander at the exact points of sampling. Size classes increase from left to right on each histogram (see also Section 20: Isoline (isopleths) pages 64-66).

Figure 14.5: Stone size distribution across a river meander

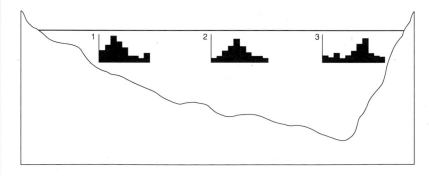

15: TRANSECTS

Transects are commonly used in fieldwork and as such deserve a section to themselves. There are several ways of displaying results collected along a transect, some have already been described in previous sections others are described here for the first time.

When to use

Most transects comprise lines or routes along which measurements/observations have been made. The measurements are taken either continuously or at regular intervals. Transects are often done when it is difficult to sample a whole area and a transect is, therefore, usually described as a sampling technique. Several transects can be combined to make an incomplete pattern.

Examples

Examples of use of transects include, changes in:

- plant species (away from a footpath, up a hillside, etc.),
- land use (with altitude, aspect, relief, etc.),
- building ages, styles and densities (with distance from a town centre),
- stone size and shape with distance down a scree slope.

Constructing transects can include a variety of forms, these include methods of collecting information described in previous sections or through specialist mapping techniques which are described below.

Methods of construction

Here you are directed to those methods of collecting information as described in previous sections.

1 If the data is continuous or sequential use a simple *line* graph (see Figure 15.1 below and pages 16-18).

2 If the data is not continuous a *scattergraph* (page 29) is often the best method. Distance along the transect should be shown as the horizontal axis. This method can only be used if the other variable is quantifiable, i.e. it is represented as a number and not a name (as in the case of plant names).

3 If a visual impression is required a *pictogram*-type graph (see pages 18-19) may be used to great effect. In the case of Figure 15.2 it is the height of the figures which represent the observed data.

4 If *profiles* or *cross sections* are involved a number of methods may be involved – see pages 44-48. A profile or cross section is used as a base with other types of graphs (line graphs, barcharts, histograms, pictograms, pie graphs, rose diagrams, etc.) superimposed.

Figure 15.1: Housing density with distance from the CBD

Worked examples

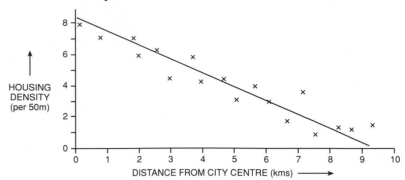

Figure 15.2: Pedestrian densities (15 minute survey) with distance from the city centre

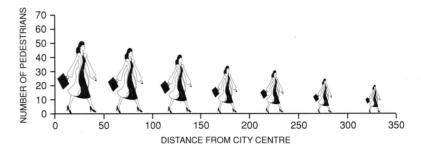

Mapping

This is one of the commonest ways of displaying transect data and involves the initial mapping of the features under study such as land use, building ages, vegetation types, soil types.

Method of construction

1 Decide on the categories you are going to include on your base map and construct a key alongside it.
2 Colour or shade in each building with its appropriate category as you take the transect. (If you decide to use colour it may be easier to complete the shading back in the classroom.)

It is often possible to combine several transects to produce a more complete picture of the study area, for example, transects of streets radiating out from a town centre which show building function, housing age and density, environmental quality, etc. The more transects you take the more accurate the overall impression your results and the more complete your map.

Worked example

Note: Transects are a type of sampling and only by covering all the area will you get a complete picture of reality.

Figure 15.3: Building ages along a street leading away from the centre of a small village

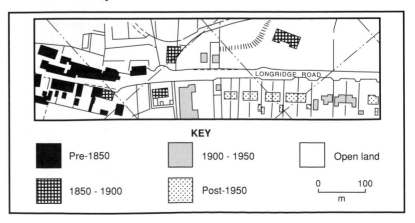

Bars

From a map

Bars can be used to simplify information on your map or when a single measurement/information has been made at regular intervals along a transect line.

Method of construction

This method 'straightens out' transect lines and makes the identification of zones more obvious.

1 Construct a block or bar to represent the length of your transect.

2 Divide these bars according to the size of each of the categories present on your map.

3 Areas that are adjacent to each other but have the same category are put together into one section (see Figure 15.4) in this way individual buildings are not shown.

Worked example

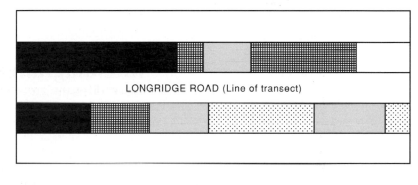

Figure 15.4: Bars represent the length of the transect shown in Figure 15.3 (the same key applies)

A single measurement/observation

Here bars are drawn from a single measurement/observation made at regular intervals along a transect line. This type of diagram can be incorporated into profiles and cross sections.

Method of construction

1 Again construct a block or bar to represent the length of your transect. Divide this bar into equal-sized sections. Each section represents one measurement/observation.

2 Devise a table alongside your bar to complete with the statistical information.

3 Take your transect, noting at regular intervals your measurement/observation.

4 Mark each measurement on the section which represents the intervals

5 Colour or shade in each of the sections

In our example transect the land use was noted at regular intervals (every 50m) up a hillside. Other relevant data such as soil variables, slope angle, aspect, altitude, were also recorded (see Figure 15.5).

Worked example

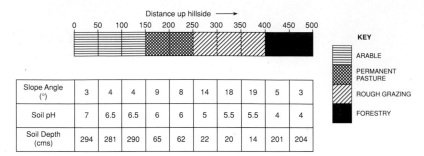

Figure 15.5: Land use transect

Slope Angle (°)	3	4	4	9	8	14	18	19	5	3
Soil pH	7	6.5	6.5	6	6	5	5.5	5.5	4	4
Soil Depth (cms)	294	281	290	65	62	22	20	14	201	204

The main weakness of this method is that there is no guarantee that a single sample at each point will reflect reality (the sample size is too small). Several transects drawn parallel to each other may give a clearer picture and even show possible zonations.

The next two methods are more reliable methods of graphical representation.

Kite diagrams

These diagrams are a more sophisticated version of the method described above. Kite diagrams are most useful when you wish to display *several* observations made at each of the sample points along your transect. They indicate where individual features occur and their relative frequencies. In this way kite diagrams provide a good visual impression of any spatial change and any associations between the individual species and/or related variables.

As with many other methods your information/data may be included alongside the kite diagram, either as a table or as another form of graph (line graph, barchart).

In the worked example below 10 plants were recorded at 1m intervals along a transect that led away from the edge of an eroded mountain footpath. The plants were sampled using a transect line and a simple point frame and gave the results shown in Table 15.1.

Table 15.1

	Distance from edge of footpath (m)										
	0	1	2	3	4	5	6	7	8	9	10
Bare earth	8	2	0	0	0	0	0	0	0	0	0
Mosses	2	1	0	1	2	0	2	1	2	0	2
Moor grass	0	6	8	4	0	0	0	0	0	0	0
Sedges	0	1	2	5	3	0	0	0	1	4	1
Bilberry	0	0	0	0	4	8	5	1	1	2	6
Heather	0	0	0	0	1	2	3	8	6	4	1

Method of construction

1 Use a separate row for each individual species found at each site. In this case there are 6 rows and, as 10 plants were sampled, each row is 10 units *wide*. The *length* of each row represents distance along the transect.

2 At each of the sample sites the width of the constructed 'kite' represents the number of times that particular plant was observed. For example, 1m away from the footpath, moorgrass was observed 6 times and so at that point the moorgrass row is 6 units wide.

3 For each sample site centralise the widths of the measurements around the central axis as shown in Figure 15.6.

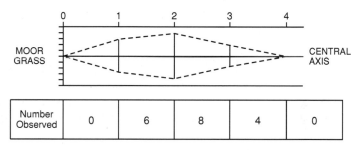

Figure 15.6: Construction of a basic kite diagram

4 Join these lines to give the 'kite' appearance. Displaying the observations in this way suggests a gradual change from sample point to sample point.

5 Using one shade (Figure 15.7) or different colours for each row can prove visually attractive.

Worked example

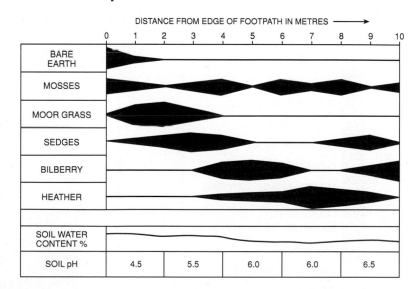

Figure 15.7: Frequencies of species along a transect

Block graphs

These are very similar to kite diagrams because they show the change in the observed variables with distance along a transect. There is, however, one important difference, block graphs use observations that have been made *continuously* along the transect rather than at regular *intervals* and, therefore, offer a more accurate picture of reality.

Method of construction

The method of construction is best described by showing a worked example.

1   An urban transect of building and land use, starting in the city centre (i.e. where there is a peak in land value) and finishing near the periphery of the CBD was taken.

2   The transect was divided into regular intervals (every 50m) and the functions of the land/building use along each of the intervals was noted and categorised. (The categories were shaded and a key provided.) Each shop frontage was measured and noted.

3   A graph was drawn up which showed the building/land use type as a percentage on the vertical scale and the distance from peak land value was shown in metres along the horizontal scale.

4   The categories in each 50m stretch were summed and converted into a percentage of the total. This percentage was drawn onto the graph. On the finished block graph each 50m stretch is represented as 100%, which is then sub-divided into the components found within that 50m (Figure 15.8).

This type of graph could be said to be a histogram version of the composite barcharts described on page 25.

Worked example

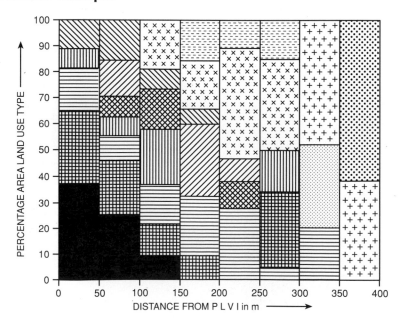

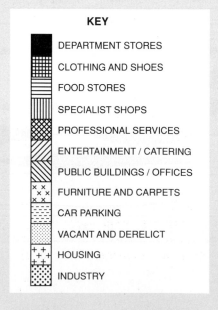

Figure 15.8: A town transect showing changes in land use

16: DOT MAPS

Maps in general

A map can be said to be a scaled down version of reality with the various properties represented symbolically. It is a basic technique for fieldworkers to be able to use and manipulate different types of information on maps. These ensuing products become a 'visual description'. They are most useful because information collected in the field often shows some form of spatial distribution when displayed on maps. There are two major categories of map.

1   Maps that show variations in non-numerical variables such as geology, land use, national parks, etc. These **'Qualitative maps'** are relatively straightforward and thus are not dealt with here.

2   Maps that show variations in numerical values (observed data) over a given area are called **Quantitative maps.** There are several different ways of representing quantitative data on outline/base maps. The various ways are dealt with here and in the following sections (up to and including Section 20).

Dot maps

One of the simplest ways certain data may be shown on a map is to draw dots which illustrate the distribution of features. These may include: crop yields, number of people, cattle, shops. If the number of data points is small and their exact location is known, the dots are drawn as 'point patterns', i.e. at the exact location where the data was collected (Figure 16.1).

In many cases, however, the information is only available for areas and not specific points. Here it is necessary to produce an approximate spread of points. This spread will represent the desired density by the spacing of the points.

It is rare for the data to be represented by a single dot. The dots must, therefore, be assigned values that are related to the total observed data. You must decide upon your choice of values (and the actual size and distribution) very carefully because they can affect the effectiveness of your final map.

Dot values
The number of items shown by each of the dots will depend on the scale of the map and the total number of items involved. As a general guide divide the total number of items by your total number of dots. For example, if there are 300 000 people/sheep/cattle, and you wish to use 500 dots then obviously each dot equals 600 items (see Figure 16.2).

Dot size
The best effects are often brought about by trial and error or practice and experience. If your dots are too large they will overcrowd the map, if too small they may not be clearly visible. In areas of greatest observed density the dots should appear to merge (Figure 16.3).

Figure 16.1: Schools using Hothersall Lodge - academic year 1986-87

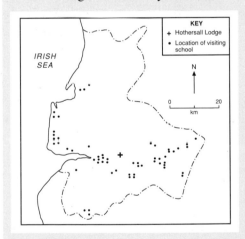

Dot location

If you wish your information to represent areas rather than specific locations then spread your dots evenly throughout that area (Figure 16.2). Dots must be placed close to any boundaries (field, parish, etc.), otherwise these areas may stand out as 'empty areas' on the map which is not really the case.

Use colour or different symbols in order to compare/contrast the distribution of several different categories on one map, for example, the distribution of ethnic groups in an urban conurbation.

Dot maps can be drawn quite quickly and are easy to produce if planned carefully beforehand. They give a good general impression of changes in density from place to place, however, the one drawback is that when large dot values are used, they have a low level of accuracy.

Worked examples

Figure 16.2: Distribution of blackface sheep in receipt of hill sheep subsidies in Scotland. Source: Carlyle, 1972

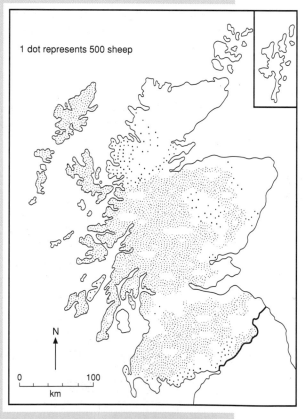

Figure 16.3: Limestone pavement distribution. Source: after Ward and Evans, 1982

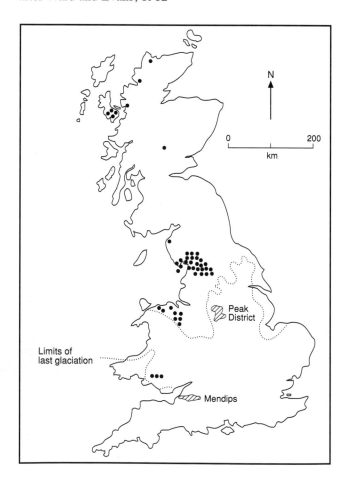

17: PROPORTIONAL SYMBOLS

Here the symbols drawn on the map are proportional in size to the observed data. Appropriate types of symbol include bars, composite bars, circles, divided circles (pie graphs), spheres, squares and pictograms. The main difficulty with this technique is to choose an appropriate scale. In theory one of the simplest methods is to use a scale line as shown on page 58. In practice the two most common methods used are proportional bars and proportional circles.

Proportional bars

The length of the bar is proportional to the observed value, but work this out carefully. You may also need to reassess the size of your base map. Draw your bars too long and they may overcrowd the map; too short and the differences are not always easily discerned. Bars should be uniform in width. Draw the base of the bar at the location it represents.

Bars often have **component categories.** If this is the case subdivide them in the same way as composite or multiple bars (see Figure 17.1 and pages 24 and 25). If there are no component categories the bars should be shaded in the same way (usually solid black).

It is equally possible to use bargraph and histogram data on base maps to show spatial patterns (Figure 17.2). Remember shading must be uniform throughout and include a key.

Worked examples

During 1985 visitors to Fairsnape Fell access area were interviewed, their point of origin and how many times they visited the area in a year was noted. Figure 17.1 below was constructed to show the results.

Figure 17.1: Visitors to Fairsnape Fell, Bowland in 1985

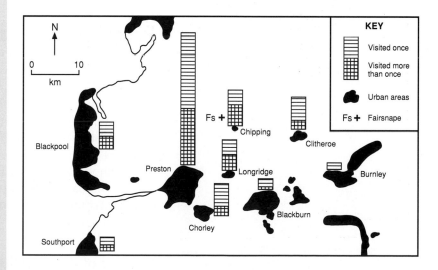

Figure 17.2: Variation in wealth in 13 Hampshire villages, 1665. Source: Pooley and Pooley, 1982

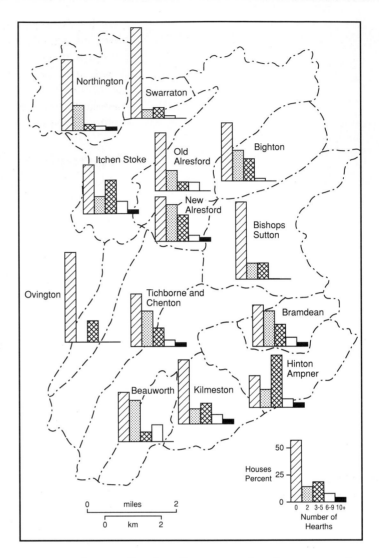

Proportional circles and pie graphs

These are the most common types of symbol used on base maps and can take several forms. The section on pie graphs discusses the problem of scale (page 26). To recap, the radius of the circles is not directly related to the observed value, once a suitable scale has been established the square root must be used. It is very unlikely that the square root of the actual observed value will provide the best circle size to fit onto your base map, therefore, a scale line is usually used. This method ensures that the optimum circle size is chosen for the scale of the base map. Circles that are too small fail to show enough detail whilst those drawn too large either will not fit onto the map or will overlap badly.

Method of construction

A square root scale

1 Draw a linear scale which accommodates all the square root values of the observed data.

Figure 17.3: A basic square root scale

2 At the far right-hand end of the scale (i.e. the largest data point) draw the largest circle that fits neatly onto your base map. From the centre of this circle draw a straight line connecting it to the left-hand end of the linear scale line (see Figure 17.4).

You have now constructed a scale line from which all the other circles' radii can be read.

3 Do this by finding the square root value of the observed data along the base line and then measuring the distance between the two lines as shown in Figure 17.4. In this example an observed value of 52 gives a square root of 7.21, the radius of the circle is measured off as 6mm.

All the resulting circles are proportional to each other and present an accurate representation of the observed data.

Figure 17.4

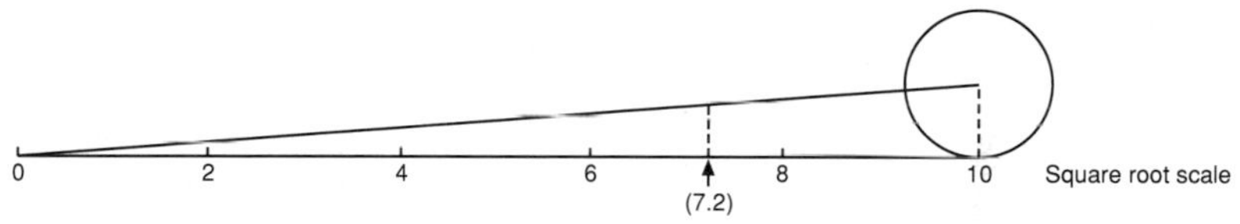

Drawing the circles on the base map
1 Start by drawing the largest value onto the map.

2 Work away from this one fitting the other circles around it. Place each circle with its centre over the site where the data was collected. If necessary overlap circles to hide parts of one behind another (see Figures 17.6 and 17.7) even where a small section of one circle shows it should be sufficient to convey the right impression. This technique is often useful in highlighting areas of high density.

If your data is shown as single/undivided circles omit all other details from inside the circles, for example, boundary lines, rivers, roads. In practice it is easiest to draw the circles first and add the background map details afterwards.

Displaying the scale
You can draw a simple scale line, however, it is common practice to show the scale as a nested set of circles (Figure 17.5). Construct these in the same way as for scale lines. The optimum size is chosen for the largest circle and the remainder are constructed according to their square root value. Often a scale line is drawn first and a sample number of circles are then taken to make up the nested set.

Note: If pie graphs (divided circles) are to be used do not overlap.

Note: Proportional circles on maps can be shaded in black or hatched but as a general rule leave them blank.

Figure 17.5

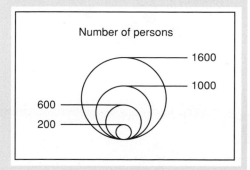

Number of persons

- 1600
- 1000
- 600
- 200

Worked examples

Figure 17.6: Regional distribution of unemployment in the UK, 1979 and 1983. Source: Mounfield, 1984

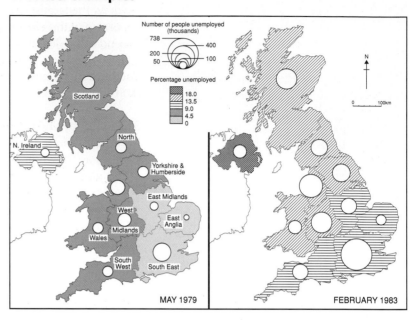

Figure 17.7: Cities in Latin America with populations of over 500 000. Source: Odell, 1974

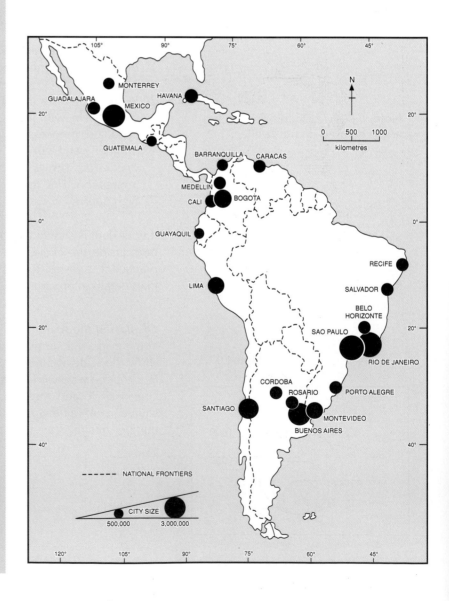

18: PIE GRAPHS/DIVIDED CIRCLES

When your observed data has definite component categories it is desirable to divide the proportional circles. It is easy to display this additional information by dividing the circles into segments. Each segment represents the relative proportions of its component category, for example, on a map showing employment structure you may divide it by the primary, secondary or tertiary industries (Figure 18.1).

The method of dividing the circles is explained in detail in Section 9: Pie Graphs on pages 26-28 and 58-60.

Proportional circles have an added advantage in that they use square root values. This means that a large range of values can be easily displayed (Figure 18.2). If you draw the pie graphs/proportional circles on your base map carefully they are visually attractive. The main drawback of this technique is that the maps are time consuming to construct.

Worked examples

Figure 18.1: Employment structure in Portugal 1970. Source: Lewis and Williams, 1982

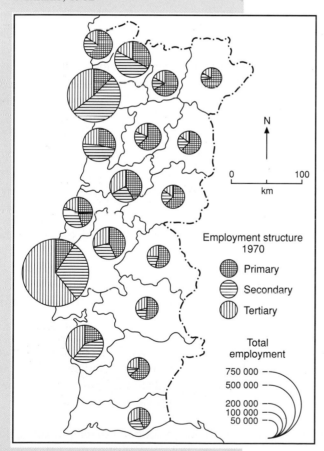

Figure 18.2: Markets for coal by region in 1977. Source: Spooner, 1981

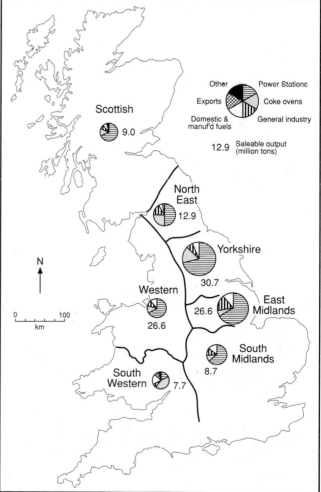

19: CHOROPLETH MAPS

Choropleth (shaded) maps are constructed using predetermined shading according to a key. The intensity of the shading indicates the size of the data values. There are two important considerations when using these types of map.

1 The information must be presented in a certain format. Different sized areas will appear on the map (counties, districts, fields, etc.) so the data must be in the form of proportions or expressed in terms of area or density. This eliminates the problem of the different areas being different sizes.

2 The data must be classified into a key using a logical and systematic method because the categories in the key must reflect the nature of the data. The different ways of classifying data into categories are discussed on pages 14-15.

Method of construction

1 Select and construct a base map that shows the internal boundaries between the areas studied (fields, parishes, etc.). The smaller these units the more accurate the map.

Figure 19.1: (a) inter-area boundaries omitted

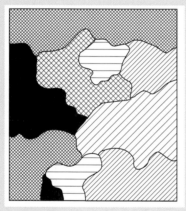

2 Work out an appropriate key taking care that no single value can appear in more than one category, for example, categories should be 2-3.9, 4-5.9, rather than 2-4, 4-6. For best visual results you should use more than three shading types but less than ten. Follow the simple rule of the darker the shading the greater the value. If you intend to use colour it is best to use groups of colours from the spectrum such as:

Red	**High value**	Violet
Orange	↑	Blue
Yellow	↓	Green
White	Low value	Yellow

If you do decide to include white, be warned: its use does present the following difficulties:

*   it is often used for areas where data is unavailable, and
*   it is impossible to tell whether an area has been left white in error or on purpose.

3 Shade in the areas according to your key. It is common practice where adjacent areas have the same type of shading to leave out the boundary between them – see Figure 19.1(a). But you may choose to include adjacent area boundaries as in Figure 19.1(b).

Figure 19.1: (b) boundaries included

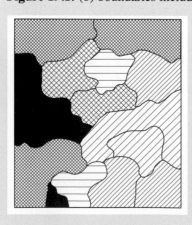

4 Draw and label your key. It should include the shading/colours, the range of values and, if possible, the number of each points in each of the categories.

Limitations of use

Choropleth maps are easy to construct. They also give a good visual impression of change over area and, because of this, they are commonly used by geographers (see Figures 19.2 and 19.3). However, the use of choropleth maps has drawbacks.

- They give an unavoidably false impression of abrupt change at the boundaries of each area.
- Variations within each of the areas mapped are not shown. Where variations do exist you will find mapping smaller area units better than mapping large ones.

Worked examples

Figure 19.2: Population changes, Lancashire District Councils, 1971-81

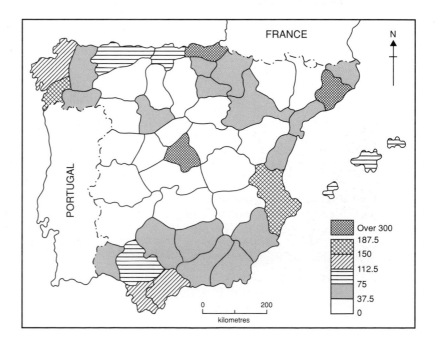

Figure 19.3: Spain: population densities per sq km, 1970. Source: Pullinger, 1981

20: ISOLINE (ISOPLETH) MAPS

When to use

Note: Isoline maps are unsuitable for use where the distribution of data is patchy.

To construct isolines you simply draw lines that join points of equal value which have been plotted on a base map. The construction of isolines is a skill that comes only with practice or trial and error.

This type of map is at its best when data is measured at precise points or locations. Points, chosen either at random or at regular intervals, are plotted onto a base map. Lines joining points of equal measurements are added, these will enable you to identify a gradual change over space. Furthermore, this type of mapping avoids the unreal effect that boundary lines produce on choropleth maps (see previous section). For isoline mapping to be effective you must collect a large amount of data. Other problems associated with using isoline maps are discussed in detail below.

Examples

The best example is a contour line which joins points of equal height, but many other measurements may be marked in the same way: Isobars (air pressure), Isotherms (temperature), Isohyets (rainfall), Isovels (velocity). *Iso* means equal, hence Iso*therm (therm* means temperature), translates as 'equal temperature'.

Method of construction

1 Mark on the base map your observed values. Ensure you have located them accurately, i.e. at the exact position you collected the data. Avoid representing areas rather than exact points – this causes problems. The more points you mark the more accurate the end result.

2 Decide on suitable values for the isolines by looking at the range you have collected. You will have to work out how many lines will fit neatly onto the map between your maximum and minimum values. Usually a fixed interval is most appropriate, for example, every 10m on a contour map. However, it is occasionally more appropriate to look for natural breaks in the dispersion of points (see Section 4: Ways of Classifying Data on pages 14-15).

3 Construct the isolines. This is the most difficult stage because few lines will pass directly through any of the observed data points. In this case it is necessary to determine the values of intermediate points through which the isoline will pass using 'logical **interpolation'.** Here an isoline is drawn at a calculated distance between two existing points, for example, we need to draw an isoline with a value of 20 between two points of 19.5 and 21. We must draw the isoline one-third of the way from the lower value (19.5) and two-thirds from the higher value (21) – see Figure 20.1.

Figure 20.1: Logical interpolation: an isoline drawn between two points of value. See Figure 20.2 for a fully worked example

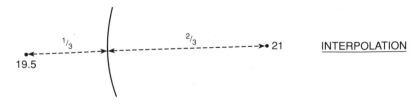

Where there are two or more possible alternative logical interpolations you can use one of two methods of locating which way the isoline goes. The first method is to estimate a 'missing' value by calculating the mean (average) of all the values around the missing point. Locate this mean value as a 'dummy spot' centrally between the actual observed points, it may indicate which way the isoline goes. The second method is to re-sample the area and include more intervening points. The latter approach is only possible with certain data because some values change over time, for example, pedestrian movements, stream velocities.

Finally, a prior knowledge of certain phenomena is helpful for those of you intending to use isolines.

- Isobars tend to be circular around low pressure systems but straighter between fronts.
- It may be desirable to shade or colour between the isolines in order to highlight change over space. The higher the value the darker or more intense the shading. This is the system used in many atlases for showing relief.
- If space allows mark on the values of each isoline, if not, then put in a sample number (e.g. every second line). Where shading is used don't forget to include a key.

Problems with use

1 The assumption is made on isoline maps that gradual change exists between any two observed values, i.e. only intermediate values and never any larger or smaller ones. In reality this may not be the case.
2 Isoline maps are only valid if a large sample is involved and collection of the amount of data required may be difficult. If a small number of points are sampled the impression of accuracy on the resulting map is false.
3 There is an element of personal judgement involved in drawing isolines. Two students using the same data may not produce identical isoline maps.
4 There is a tendency to try to 'force' lines just to complete a pattern which may appear to be emerging. The data may not allow for this forcing so try to avoid this situation.

Worked examples

Velocity readings, taken at regular intervals and depths across a river meander, were plotted onto an accurate cross section of the feature and isovels were interpolated (see Figure 20.2).

Figure 20.2: Isovels on a river meander (River Langden). Figures are in metres per second

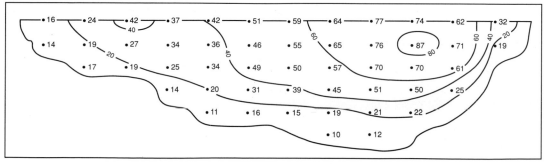

FIGURES IN METRES PER SECOND

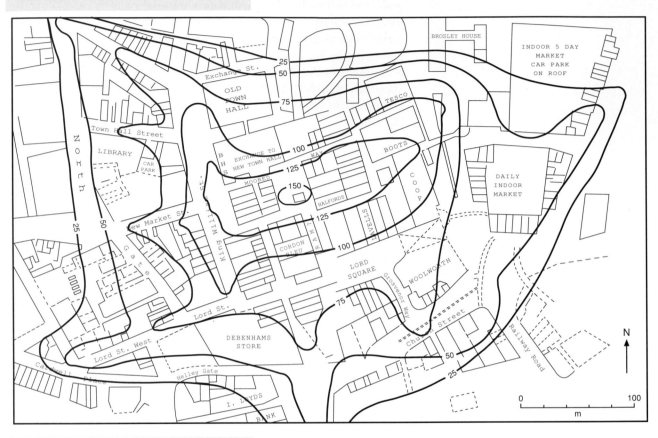

21: THE LOCATION QUOTIENT

When to use

There are numerous ways of showing spatial variation of data, the most common being the use of different types of map. In some circumstances it may be desirable to emphasise certain characteristics of the observed data. This can be achieved by a combination of statistics and cartography (map construction).

The Location Quotient (LQ) is used to indicate the degrees of concentration of one particular activity/characteristic within a chosen area, for example, the concentrations of rented accommodation in a city centre.

Examples

Plant or animal species within a particular community: human activities (occupation, religion, ethnic group) within an area/settlement; shopping types within a CBD.

Method of construction

1 First calculate the statistics using Equation 21.1. The final figure (the locational quotient) is the ratio between the percentage of a specific group (within a given area) and the percentage of the whole group or population for that area.

In this example the total rented accommodation in a specific area of a town is 28% but the area has only 7% of the town's total housing.

$$\text{LQ for the area} = \frac{\% \text{ rented accommodation in the area}}{\% \text{ total housing in the area}}$$

$$= \frac{28}{7}$$

Equation 21.1

$$= 4.0$$

The LQ for all the other areas under study is calculated in the same way.

2 The results are put onto a choropleth map using the method described on pages 62 and 63 (see e.g. Figure 21.1). Don't forget to include a key.

Figure 21.1: The location quotient for rented accommodation in the Borough of Greater London

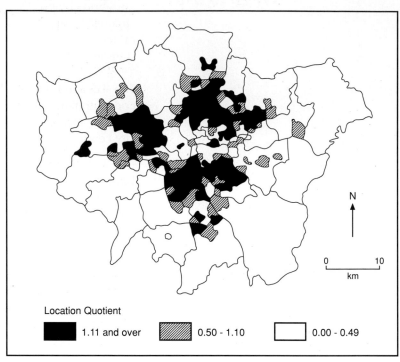

In theory the LQ ranges from zero to infinity. If an area has a value of more than 1.0 then the subgroup (rented accommodation) is over-represented within that area. The larger the value the greater the concentration of the subgroup. In Figure 21.1 the areas shaded black are over-represented, the areas shaded white are under-represented and those cross-hatched are on the borderline between the two.

When to use

Most of the methods already described refer to information collected at definite, stationary, points. Sometimes the information we wish to show is mobile.

Examples

Traffic and pedestrian flows, human and animal migrations, diffusion of innovations and ideas, movement of goods and services.

Methods of construction

In the case of mapping movements there are several methods of construction that can be used, the final choice of method depends upon the type and suitability of the data you have collected. These include: composite bars, flow lines and desire lines, each is dealt with separately below.

Composite bars

The principle of construction is the same as for Composite barcharts in Section 8: More Barcharts and Histograms on pages 22-25. The length of the bar represents the **total** volume observed and it is subdivided into component categories according to their relative proportions. The arrow head at the end of the bar indicates the direction of the movement. Figure 22.1 shows the numbers, composition and direction of traffic flow around a roundabout.

The selection of an appropriate scale is important and may prove a little difficult to work out. The separate components may be indicated as colours or shadings. A key must be included because it is unlikely that labels will fit onto your base map.

Worked example

A detailed traffic survey was conducted to try to identify traffic flow around a well known 'trouble' spot. It was carried out between 9.00 and 9.30a.m. on Thursday 10 January. The results are shown as composite bars in Figure 22.1.

Figure 22.1: Traffic flow at Stonebridge roundabout, Longridge

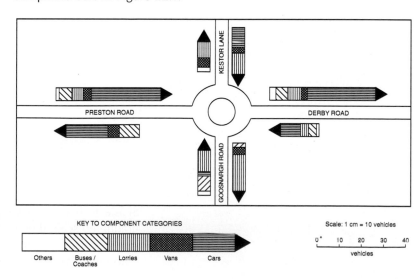

Flow lines

These are used when we are interested in the *total volume* of the flow and not in any of the component category values. Here the *width* of the line represents the total observed volume (and not the length as above). Flow lines are most effective when only one type of information is involved, for example, pedestrian flow.

The most difficult part of this technique is working out an appropriate scale to cover all of your observed values. There are three alternatives:

1 A simple proportional scale where the width of the line is related directly to the observed value (Figure 22.2(a)).

2 A more complex proportional scale (Figure 22.2(b)) using the square root or the logarithmic value of the observed data. This is often necessary where the range of values is high thus making the type of scale described in 1 above, impractical (see Section 13: Logarithmic Graphs – pages 41-43).

3 A graduated scale (Figure 22.2(c)). Here a number of fixed line widths are used and the data values are categorised according to these widths.

Figures 22.2 to 22.4 show these three types of scale. They indicate clearly that the first method is the only one which allows quantitative interpretation (reading values off the finished map) to be easily carried out.

Note: In simple and complex proportional scales changes are shown as a gradual change in the width of the line. When a graduated scale is used (pre-determined category sizes) the widths of the lines change abruptly halfway between sample points. This gives the visual impression of abrupt changes in flow rather than the reality of gradual changes. Figure 22.3 indicates these differences clearly.

Figure 22.2: Flow lines (a) a simple proportional scale, (b) a more complex proportional scale, and (c) a graduated scale

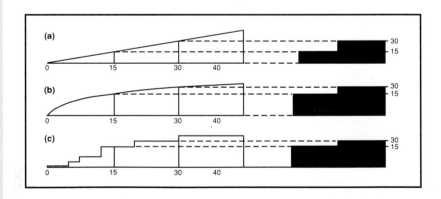

Figure 22.3: (a) Proportional and (b) graduated scales

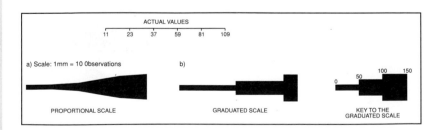

Shade in black to clearly highlight the flow. If you choose to use a graduated scale then your class differences do not have to be uniform but the width of the actual lines must increase steadily by equal amounts. Finally, it is a good idea to keep the number of size classes small when using flow lines.

Worked example

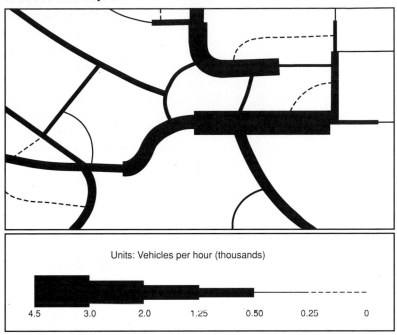

Figure 22.4: Traffic flow using a graduated scale

Units: Vehicles per hour (thousands)

| 4.5 | 3.0 | 2.0 | 1.25 | 0.50 | 0.25 | 0 |

Two directional flow

Sometimes it is desirable to show two-directional flow, e.g. traffic travelling in different directions along the same route. Flow line maps can be easily adapted to show this data.

Two flow lines are drawn for each routeway observed with arrow heads indicating the direction of flow. Break the flow lines into separate sections in order to eliminate overlap that occurs at junctions. This simplifies the overall appearance of the finished map.

Figure 22.5 shows the pattern for pedestrian flows in a modern shopping centre using a simple proportional scale since the range of values is relatively small.

Figure 22.5: Two directional flow of pedestrians

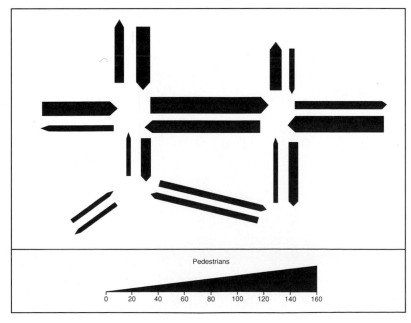

Pedestrians

0 20 40 60 80 100 120 140 160

Desire lines

This simple technique is used to illustrate the direction and scale of movement between areas or points of origin and destination. Desire lines are especially useful for illustrating spheres of influence, hinterlands and catchment areas.

Draw a straight line to indicate each individual movement between the different places. The length represents the *straight line distance* between the two places. If there is more than one movement then represent the number of movements by the thickness of the line.

Desire line maps can become very crowded and complex where large amounts of data are involved. This is especially true if just a single destination point is involved. You can overcome this problem by drawing a small circle around the destination point and excluding all lines that fall within it. The example shown in Figure 22.6 involves a single destination (Hothersall Lodge). However, where several destinations are involved more complex diagrams can be constructed, for example, different service centres, places of entertainment, schools, colleges.

Worked example

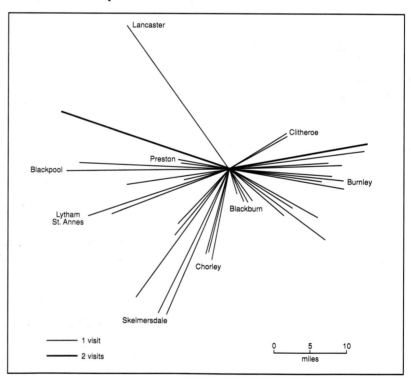

Note: Flow lines involve the movement of people, goods, etc., and the movement of innovations, ideas and information, so they are relevant to the understanding of communication networks.

Figure 22.6: Schools attending residential courses at Hothersall Lodge 1983-84

APPENDIX 1 - CALCULATIONS FOR CONSTRUCTING COMPOSITE BARCHARTS

Table 1 shows the calculations for the percentages of component categories in preparation for constructing composite barcharts on page 25. This was done using the following equation:

$$\frac{\text{Actual number in category}}{\text{Actual total number}} \times 100$$

= percentage of each component category

Year	Component categories of total data						
	Ford actual percentage		**Leyland** actual percentage		**Vauxhall** actual percentage		**Actual total**
1972	22	$\frac{22}{67} \times 100 = 32$	30	$\frac{30}{67} \times 100 = 46$	15	$\frac{15}{67} \times 100 = 22$	67
1973	33	$\frac{33}{71} \times 100 = 45$	24	$\frac{24}{71} \times 100 = 30$	14	$\frac{14}{71} \times 100 = 25$	71
1974	44	$\frac{44}{79} \times 100 = 56$	20	$\frac{20}{79} \times 100 = 25$	15	$\frac{15}{79} \times 100 = 19$	79
1975	49	$\frac{49}{84} \times 100 = 58$	18	$\frac{18}{84} \times 100 = 22$	17	$\frac{17}{84} \times 100 = 20$	84
1976	50	$\frac{50}{86} \times 100 = 57$	16	$\frac{16}{86} \times 100 = 16$	20	$\frac{20}{86} \times 100 = 23$	86

Table 1: Cars sold in Clitheroe (1972-76)

The percentage calculated can now be drawn on a percentage composite barchart (see page 25). The bars are all drawn the same length and, therefore, do not reflect the overall total trend, i.e. overall car sales increased over the time period. What the graph does show is an accurate picture of the increases and decreases in sales of specific makes of car.

Throughout this book these figures have been used three times (see pages 24 and 25). Can you say which you think is the most appropriate method. Does the method depend on what you are trying to show?

APPENDIX 2 - CONSTELLATION DIAGRAMS

When to use

As already mentioned on page 12, constellation diagrams are a more sophisticated version of flow or systems diagrams. They illustrate the relative strengths that exist in the relationships between different variables within a system. Each variable must display a quantitative value so that a multiple correlation or association test can be carried out using all the variables.

Examples
Slope and soil variables, plant associations along a succession, stream flow variables.

Method of construction
A constellation diagram is three dimensional and, therefore, is very difficult to construct. But, if drawn properly, it is very useful for illustrating the dynamics within a system or the associations of variables (especially useful for illustrating plant associations).

1   Carry out a multiple correlation or association test on the observed variables. List those that show a significant relationship at your chosen level of confidence (usually 0.05). Work out the reciprocal value for these significantly paired variables.

2   Start constructing the diagram with the variable that appears to have the greatest number of significant relationships and work outwards (each variable may be put in a frame or 'box' for clarity).

3   Draw in lines between the two variables. Each line is proportional to the strength of the relationship of the two variables. The stronger their relationship the closer together the two variables should be drawn. Work out a suitable scale. Variables that show no significant relationships are not connected by a line.

Broken lines may be used to represent relationships that cannot be shown on a two dimensional graph (see Figure 1 opposite). Discrete populations or communities may be easily identified (see Figure 1).

Figure 1: Plant association along a sand dune succession. Source: Neil Adams, Blackburn Computer Centre

KEY TO PLANT SPECIES

MG = Marram grass
SS = Sand sedge
HR = Heather
MO = Moor grass
CK = Chickweed
SC = Sand couch grass
RH = Restharrow
LI = Lichen
HB = Hawkbit
SK = Seakale
HW = Hawkweed
DV = Dog violet
DB = Dewberry
MP = Marsh pennywort
RM = Reedmace
YI = Yellow Iris
TS = Thistle
CB = Cranesbill
CW = Creeping Willow

Worked example

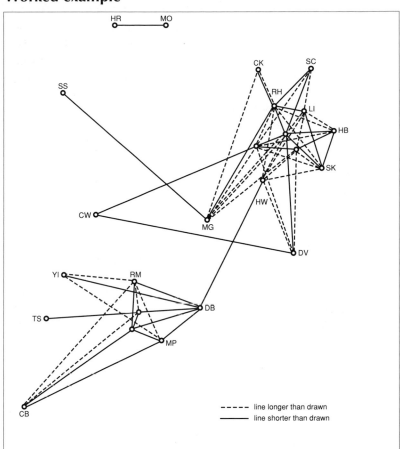

GLOSSARY OF WORDS AND TERMS

Azimuth
A compass bearing. Often compass bearing data is put into classes or groups, these are called azimuthal classes.

Component categories
Elements that make up the total or whole, for example, a traffic count may consist of component categories such as cars, lorries, etc.

Correlation
A relationship or connection between different factors or variables.

Data
Measurements or observations usually made in the field, for example stone sizes, building ages, land uses. Continuous data – information collected continuously over time and an area. Discontinuous data – information collected either at regular or at random intervals.

Hypothesis (plural hypotheses)
A statement involving an idea, often regarding a geographical concept, for example, air temperatures will decrease with altitude. Hypotheses are often used as a framework for fieldwork enquiries. Null hypothesis – the converse statement, for example, there is no connection between air temperatures and altitude.

Interpolation
The estimation of intermediate values and patterns using observed data (see pages 64-65 for one example).

Orientation
The direction a phenomena (stone, corrie) faces. Usually expressed as a compass bearing.

Proportions
The relation of one variable to another or a ratio between two quantities. These values are said to be proportional.

Qualitative
A non-numerical value or an opinion, for example, an environmental perception – 'a beautiful view'.

Quantitative
A measurement of a feature or a measurable amount, for example, the length of a stone = 10.3cm.

Standard deviation
A quantity calculated to illustrate the extent by which a group of data differs from the mean (average).

Totals
The observed data added together. There are different types: **Partial** – indicates a summing of some but not all of the data; all partial totals make up the grand total. **Accumulative** – a running total calculated as the data is systematically worked through. **Grand** – the complete end total of all the observed data.

BIBLIOGRAPHY AND FURTHER READING

References

Carlyle, W.J. (1972) 'The marketing and movement of Scottish hill lambs', *Geography,* 57, 1, pp. 10-17.

Frost, L.R. (1985) 'Second thoughts on climate graphs', *Teaching Geography,* 10, 4, pp. 162-3.

King, R.L. (1982) 'Southern Europe: dependence of development?', *Geography,* 67, 3, pp. 221-34.

Mounfield, P.R. (1984) 'The deindustrialisation and reindustrialisation of the UK', *Geography,* 69, 2, pp. 141-6.

Odell, P.R. (1974) 'Geography and economic development with special reference to Latin America', *Geography,* 59, 3, pp. 208-22.

Paterson, K. and Chambers, B. (1982) 'Techniques for the study of limestone pavements', *Teaching Geography,* 8, 1, p. 5.

Pooley, C. and Pooley, M. (1982) 'Population in the past', *Teaching Geography,* 8, 1, pp. 37-43.

Pullinger, H. (1981) 'Combining new and traditional geography: two ideas for O-level teaching', *Teaching Geography,* 6, 4, pp. 151-5.

Spooner, D.J. (1981) 'Geography of coal's second coming', *Geography,* 66, 2, pp. 29-41.

In addition, the following publication may prove useful in conjunction with this book:

St John, P. and Richardson, D. (1996) *Methods of Statistical Analysis of Fieldwork Data,* the Geographical Association.

Further reading

As explained in the introduction this manual is designed to complement existing publications on fieldwork techniques. The following titles may prove interesting.

Chalmers, N. and Parker, P. (1984) *Fieldwork and Statistics for Ecological Projects,* (OU project guide), Field Studies Council.

Dowdeswell, W.H. (1984) *Ecology – Principles and Practice,* Heinemann.

Greasley, B. (1984) *Project Fieldwork,* Bell & Hyman.

Ingle Smith, D. and Stopp, P. (1978) *The River Basin,* Cambridge University Press.

Lennon, B.J. and Cleves, P.G. (1984) *Techniques and Fieldwork in Geography,* UTP.

MESU (various) (1988) *Using Computers in Fieldwork,* MESU Publications.

Science in Geography Series (four titles), various authors (1970s) Oxford University Press.

Sources and Methods in Geography (series of six titles) various authors (1970s) Butterworth.

Warn, S. and Bottomley, C. (1986) *Fieldwork Investigations* (five titles), Arnold Wheaton.

COMPUTER SOFTWARE

As computers become more available the opportunities they provide to support the analysis of fieldwork data increases. The major benefit computers provide is to free students from mechanical and repetitive tasks thus enabling them to spend more time on the analysis and synthesis.

Many of the techniques described in this book can be achieved with a computer and appropriate software. However, it is important that students can complete any technique manually and understand it fully before they start to use the computer. One advantage of using a spreadsheet for some of the analysis in this book is that they 'teach' the spreadsheet properly by entering appropriate formulae. The resultant sheet can then be used to automate further calculations.

In the past there was a plethora of specific statistics and graphing software. Today a few tools which most schools will find available on their computers will replace this range of software. There are four classes of software to consider:

- Databases
- Spreadsheets
- Mapping or Geographic Information Systems (GIS) software
- Other specific packages

Databases
These are useful for dealing with large quantities of data where the information needs to be sorted and searched, either in one field or across two or more. Most databases provide some graphing facilities although the flexibility and range of graph types is variable.

Spreadsheets
Most commercial spreadsheets now provide a comprehensive set of statistical functions ranging from maximum, minimum and range to more complex correlations and other functions. The user has the ability to either set up tables for calculation with manually entered formulae or to use ready-made functions. Most spreadsheets also have a comprehensive set of graphing facilities, with a range of graph types which are often very flexible, with the user able to alter any element of the graph.

Mapping or GIS software
There has been considerable development in mapping and GIS software with many commercial products available. However, these tend to be expensive and are sometimes a little complex. There are two main packages available for schools. *AEGIS* (Advisory Unit) and the *Key* family of software (Anglia).

Specific statistical and graphing software
There are a number of dedicated packages available for statistical analysis and with specific graphing functionality, a few of which are mentioned below. However, a good place to start is by investigating the software your school has already.

Identify which areas of your fieldwork analysis and presentation could benefit from the use of computer software and talk to your IT co-ordinator about the functions of your school's standard database and spreadsheet software.

Publishing a list of software for school use is fraught with difficulties as such lists go out of date very quickly. The items below provide a start in the latter two categories along with some references for further information.

Mapping/GIS software
AEGIS
Key Plus

Supastat (version 3.2)

Place of Publication:	Tewkesbury
Publisher:	Software Production Associates (SPA) Ltd
Telephone:	01684 833700
Year of Publication:	1996
Machine/Version/Price:	PC; £36.00 VAT exc (School's suite); £72.00 VAT exc (Full suite)
Requires (minimum):	Windows 3.1

A data analysis suite of programs. Full suite gives an extensive set of tests designed for professional use; School's suite is a subset providing sufficient statistical power for use up to and including A-level statistics. Site licences and upgrades available.

WinLang

Author:	Knight, S.
Place of Publication:	Brighton
Publisher:	Trellis Education Software and Training
Telephone:	01273 203920
Year of Publication:	1994
Series:	Win
Machine/Version/Price:	IBM PC compatibles; 3; £60.00
Format:	Disk; manual
Requires (minimum):	Microsoft Windows 3.1+; colour monitor; mouse

A departmental assessment package designed to allow easy access to national curriculum statements, statistics reports, profiles and lists. Upgrades to NCSoft4 available. The product is specifically geared to meeting the needs of key stages 1, 2, 3 and 4 covering national curriculum subjects, English and modern languages.

1st (version 2.28)

Author:	Edwards, G.R. and Turnbull, C.
Place of Publication:	Willaston
Supplier:	Serious Statistical Software
Telephone:	0151 327 4268
Year of Publication:	1997
Machine/Version/Price:	Acorn; £150.00
Format:	2 x floppy disk; manual
Requires (minimum):	RISC OS 2; 1Mb RAM
Compatible with:	RISC PC; 1stJr; 1stL

Data analysis and manipulation software covering elementary to advanced statistical techniques. Multi-tasking, with spreadsheet-type data entry and CSV file interface to other software. Drawfile graphics. Useful for 'value added' analyses. Price is for Education only.

Specific statistical and graphing software

Graphs & Stats (version 4.0)

Author:	Rouse, Dr C.
Place of publication:	Carmarthen
Supplier:	Felingwm Systems & Software
Year of Publication:	1994
Machine/Version/Price:	PC; £50.00
Format:	Floppy disc; documentation
Requires (minimum):	486; Hard disc drive; Windows 3.1
Software works best with:	800x600 display

Contains a selection of the most commonly used statistical and graphical techniques. For simple statistical analysis and drawing of graphs. Designed for project work. Network and site licences available.

Secos (version 3)

Place of Publication:	Bishop's Stortford
Supplier:	Statistics for Education
Telephone:	01279 652183
Year of Publication:	1994
Machine/Version/Price:	PC
Format:	Floppy disc

A new version of the data-handling and graphing program which provides users with outline maps on which they can display data, using colour/shading, proportional circles or located bar graphs. Data sets are published to accompany the program.

1stJr (version 2.28)

Author:	Edwards, G.R. and Turnbull, C.
Place of Publication:	Willaston
Supplier:	Serious Statistical Software
Telephone:	0151 327 4268
Year of Publication:	1997
Machine/Version/Price:	Acorn; £84.00
Format:	2 x floppy disk; manual
Requires (minimum):	RISC OS 2; 1Mb RAM
Compatible with:	RISC PC; 1st; 1stL

A junior version (sub-set) of **1st** which is upgradable to the full **1st** system. Extra modules from **1st** can be ordered. Loan copies available. Price is for Education only. Site licences available.

Fieldworks

Publisher:	Hallsannery Field Centre
Supplier:	BTL Publishing
Telephone:	01274 841320
Year of Publication:	1997
Machine/Version/Price:	PC; £99.00 VAT exc
Format:	CD ROM
Requires (minimum):	386; 25MHz; 4Mb RAM; DOS 3.3; Windows 3.1
Software works best with:	33MHz; 4Mb+ RAM

A data package for presenting and analysing the results of fieldwork. Includes simple descriptive statistics, scattergraphs, t-tests, correlations, diversity and similarity indices.

References

Product specifically geared to meeting Key Stages 3 and 4:

Hassell, D. (1996) 'Using IT in coursework', *Teaching Geography,* 21, 2, pp. 77-80.
GA/NCET (1995) *Using IT to Enhance Geography - Case Studies at Key Stages 3 & 4.* GA/NCET.
GA/NCET (1995) *Geography and IT: Shopping and Traffic.* GA/NCET.

The Geography IT Support Project has a series of web pages on the NCET web site with further support and guidance, including some information on software http://www.ncet.org.uk

'know then fully the nature of the beast so that you may be its ruler and not its slave.'